Reshaping
physical education

Margarete Streicher

Reshaping physical education

Edited and presented by Betty E. Strutt

Translated from the German
by C.R.M. Larner

Manchester University Press

Original editions in German

© Verlag für Jugend und Volk, GMBH
Wien 1
Tiefer Graben 7–9
Austria

© 1970 English edition
(editor Betty E. Strutt)

Manchester University Press
316–324 Oxford Road
Manchester M13 9NR

GB SBN 7190 0412 8

Printed in Great Britain by
W & J Mackay & Co Ltd, Chatham, Kent

Contents

List of illustrations

List of exercises*

* Exercises in the text are inset

Foreword

Margarete Streicher was born in 1891 in Graz, Austria into a very musical family. After attending a humanistic Grammar School in Vienna she studied biology at the University of Vienna and was awarded her degree followed in 1916 by a doctorate. In order to have a second teaching subject she took a one year course in 1912 and qualified as a teacher of physical education. She taught in schools in Vienna and at a training college for women teachers; she also taught remedial gymnastics for social welfare organizations. From 1914 onwards she attended many courses in gymnastics including four months' study in Sweden in 1920, visiting the Gymnastic Institutes at Stockholm and Lund and becoming acquainted with the work of Elin Falk.

Dr Streicher came to the study of physical education with a scientific training behind her but without any previous knowledge of sport or gymnastics. She was not bound by traditions or ideologies to any form of physical activity. Whilst coming to grips with the new field of study she was able to view it in a detached manner and soon established the fact that there was a gaping abyss between theory and practice. The structure and function of the body, the physical and intellectual development of the child, etc., were studied, but this knowledge was hardly utilized at all in the practical job of teaching children. Practice was a very long way from tested knowledge.

After the first world war there was a vigorous movement for reform in education. A 'Reform Section' was created in the Austrian Ministry of Education and in 1919 Dr Karl Gaulhofer was appointed Director of the Department of Physical Education in the Ministry of Education. Dr Streicher first saw him at a meeting of teachers when the entrance examination for the training course for physical education teachers was being vigorously discussed. At the end of the session the new Director summarized the discussion and in so doing impressed her with his great intellectual ability. Not long after this Dr Gaulhofer saw Dr Streicher teaching a class of thirteen year old girls and he later recalled that as he watched her sure, lively, natural method of teaching he suddenly realized that while he had been trying to discover what constituted a natural method of physical education, here in Vienna a young woman teacher was already putting such a method into practice. All at once everything that was problematic vanished and he saw the way which had to be followed. From that time their working together started—a constant give and take—and it was sometimes impossible to know who was the first to grasp an idea. This co-operation continued until Dr Gaulhofer left Austria.

Karl Gaulhofer was born in Styria, Austria in 1885 and died in Amsterdam in 1941. He studied botany at the University of Graz from 1903 to 1909 and was awarded his doctorate. During those years at Graz he also took the Ministry of Education examination in gymnastics. He taught in a secondary school until 1914. After the war he took up his appointment with the Ministry of Education; he was also Director of the Training Department for teachers of physical education at the University of Vienna with a Professorship in Theory and Teaching Method of Physical Education. He held both appointments until he moved to Amsterdam in 1932 to become Rector of the Academy for Physical Education.

During his time at the University of Vienna and with the Ministry of Education the reforms carried out by Dr Gaulhofer, in close association with Dr Streicher, were aimed at integrating physical education with education as a whole, and building a scientific theory of physical education. He gave greater depth to the whole training in physical and higher education of teachers, both general and specialist. Large-scale increases were made in facilities, the number of physical education lessons was raised and improvements were made in the school medical services.

In 1918 Dr Streicher was appointed to the staff of the Institute of Physical Education at the University of Vienna to teach practical subjects such as gymnastics, swimming and games. In 1921 she became responsible for Theory of Method at the Institute and also took charge of the practical teaching of women students. From 1931 she took over from Dr Gaulhofer the main lecture courses at the Institute for General and Applied Teaching Method and the seminars connected with these courses. She lectured in Austria and abroad, often in Germany; in London in 1934 as a guest of the Ling Association of Physical Education when she gave a number of lectures on Austrian School Physical Education; in 1935 at Oxford as a guest of the Medical Gymnastic Teachers Association, and in 1937 at the Seventh Congress of the Stockholm Gymnastic Central Institute.

From 1924 to 1938 Dr Streicher was Inspector of Girls' Physical Education for Vienna—middle schools, commercial schools and colleges, and teacher training colleges for women, and 'kept an eye on' private schools of gymnastics and physical education. In 1938, the beginning of the National Socialist era in Austria, she resigned from the Inspectorate and tended to remain in the background until the end of the war. By 1951 she was again active in the training of teachers of physical education, was an Honorary lecturer at the Institute of Physical Education of the University of Vienna and a frequent contributor to *Leibesübungen und Leibeserziehung*, the official journal of the Austrian Institutes of Physical Education.*

Both Dr Gaulhofer and Dr Streicher were trained in scientific disciplines but the former had a tradition of gymnastics behind him and looked there for the way into the future. As for Dr Streicher she quotes Rilke when assessing her own position: 'Nothing has come into existence until I have seen it'—thus they were able to complement each other's viewpoints.

In another way their co-operation was important, for as Dr Streicher has said, so many major issues are looked at as if there were only men in the world and then afterwards amendments are made to accommodate women. From the outset Dr Gaulhofer and Dr Streicher thought in two directions. The picture seen through the stereoscope gives the solution: from each of two different points a picture is taken and the two pictures are then combined through a lens. In this way a picture is created which is three dimensional and real.

For Dr Streicher their work together was like taking stock of new territory—a general view had to be found, the basic facts had to be ascertained and order created. This led to sharply formulated aphorisms such as: 'The body is the point of attack, the whole man is the target', or: 'Physical education must reckon with the

---

* Biographical material Margarete Streicher from *Leibesübungen und Leibeserziehung*, V, 3, pp. 1–6, March 1951, Vienna.
XX, 6, pp. 5–8, June 1966 and XX, 7, p. 11, September 1966, Vienna.
Biographical material Karl Gaulhofer from *Österreiches Biographisches Lexikon*, Vol. I, p. 412, 1957.

favourable and the unfavourable effects of the daily round of work and play'. The educational attitude had to prevail in every detail —an example is the reversal of the question: 'For which branch of sport is a person suited?' to the question: 'Which branch of practical activity does a person need in order to attain maximum development?'

In 1966 at the celebration of the renewal of her doctorate Dr Streicher said that she had been awarded her doctorate in recognition of her scientific work. She made the point that the scientific character of physical education as an independent subject is still doubted today, and added that one should avoid saying that physical education *is* or *is not* science; rather one ought to say that there is scientific work in the field of physical education—and by scientific she means an independent, well-organized branch of knowledge capable of supporting research—in this way it would be much easier to reach agreement. Not every practising doctor is a scientist, similarly it has never been maintained that every physical education teacher is one. Dr Streicher herself throughout her life has striven quite consciously to do scientific work and her writings stand as a record of her achievement.

This English presentation of the writings of Margarete Streicher is not a straight translation from German to English of a single book. Her writings are contained in six volumes; the first published in 1922 was the work of Dr Gaulhofer and Dr Streicher, *Outlines of Austrian Elementary Physical Education.** (This book was completely revised in 1959 by Dr Streicher who then added Section III.) Volumes of collected essays followed, *Natural Gymnastics*** Volumes I, II, and III which included essays by Dr Gaulhofer and Dr Streicher. Volumes IV and V, published in 1956 and 1959, were collections of later essays.

To produce the present volume a selection was made from Section III of *Outlines of Austrian Elementary Physical Education* and from essays written by Dr Streicher contained in Volumes I, II, III, and V of *Natural Gymnastics*. (Volume IV is concerned exclusively with the application of the work in Austria.) As the essays were written over a period of thirty-seven years, from 1922 to 1959, the later essays repeated and amplified the main aspects of the work which had been covered in earlier essays.

* Grundzüge des österreichischen Schulturnens.
** Natürliches Turnen.

In this book the chief areas of discussion are collected into three sections each containing a number of chapters. A chapter may consist of only one essay but most of the chapters have been prepared from two or more essays where it was thought that this would clarify the subject under discussion. References to the essays and parts of essays used in each section are given at the end of the book.

The original essays were written specifically for teachers of physical education in Austria—primary school teachers who were non-specialists and specialist teachers of the subject in secondary schools. Dr Streicher's theory and practice of physical education is securely based on sound biological foundations but she also brings brilliant personal insight into the many highly subjective matters about which she writes. A presentation of her work to an English-speaking audience seems appropriate at a time when physical education is being expanded and enriched by psychological, sociological and aesthetic ideas. Dr Streicher embodies in her writings many of the changes that have taken place in teaching the subject in this country including the development of a wider spectrum of movement in education; at the same time she gives teachers a sound scientific basis.

This book is not the first introduction to England of the Austrian approach to physical education. In addition to Dr Streicher's own lectures, 'Austrian gymnastics'* was brought to this country in 1924 when Miss Margaret Oldland returned to the staff of Chelsea College of Physical Education after a year of study in Germany, and in Austria at the University of Vienna where Dr Streicher and Dr Gaulhofer were teaching. Miss Oldland's enthusiasm for their work made the Principal, Miss Dorette Wilkie, and staff eager for her to introduce it at the college; she therefore taught second-year students and also held classes for past students of the college which aroused great interest. Regrettably this continued for only six months as Miss Oldland died in February, 1925.

In the early 1930's, with Miss May Fountain now Principal, a link was again made with Dr Streicher through a former pupil of hers teaching in London, Miss Maria Ebner. In 1932 a senior member of the staff, Miss Ruth Clark, visited Vienna to observe

* *Journal of Physical Education.* XXXVIII, 115, pp. 117–24, November 1946, London.

the work at the University and in schools; on her return she experimented with it in the teaching of first-year students. Dr Streicher later visited the college so that the staff were able to have discussions with her and see her teach some classes. Experiment with Austrian gymnastics for school children made little progress until the war when the college had the unique opportunity of supervising all the gymnastics at Ardwyn School, Aberystwyth, over six consecutive years; this convinced the staff that they were fully justified in using this type of work with girls.

Miss Fountain and Miss Clark retired as Principal and Deputy Principal of the college in 1950; up to that time all students began their gymnastic training with Austrian gymnastics and work influenced by Austrian principles, and some students experienced a further period of it in their third and final year. Undoubtedly through the staff and generations of students trained at Chelsea College of Physical Education Dr Streicher's work has influenced many women teachers of physical education in this country but progress has been handicapped by the lack of a translation of her writings.

The present volume is the best substitute for the original books and it should help to make available to English-speaking people the theory and philosophy of Dr Streicher. Her writing has a freshness of approach which has not become stale or out-of-date and her emphasis on the development of the individual child speaks to us today. Dr Streicher's ideas on teaching children up to the age of ten or eleven are entirely consistent with the views of educationalists and teachers who are concerned with primary education. At this stage the teacher tells the children what to do, sets them the task, and then allows them to work out by themselves how they will do it.

At the present time, when it is not easy to retain the interest and co-operation of many teenage boys and girls in games and gymnastics, Dr Streicher's understanding of their stage of development and her assessment of their needs in physical education should be welcomed by teachers. She gives clear, definite suggestions on teaching this age group, the suitability of different kinds of physical activity and the necessity of involving them intellectually as well as physically in the work.

Dr Streicher has a common sense view of the many and various facets of movement education that have from time to time been over emphasized in this or that theory of physical education—the development of physical skills, strength, mobility and flexibility, fitness, creative movement. All these different facets of the work have their place but her chief concern is with the full development of the individual child; thus all the strands have to be used, they come together in the service of education. It is my belief that Dr Streicher's work may help to give a better understanding of what we are doing in physical education and why we are doing it; she weaves the subject into the whole texture of education; it is a vital link necessary for growth to full physical and intellectual maturity.

Betty E. Strutt

Department of Physical Education
University of Manchester

Acknowledgements

It is a pleasant duty to put on record my gratitude to all who have helped me in the preparation of this book. First Miss May Fountain and Miss Ruth Clark who suggested to me the idea of an English book on the writings of Dr Streicher and throughout the long period of preparation have given generously of their knowledge and understanding of Dr Streicher's work and have been a constant source of encouragement and help. Next I must express my admiration and gratitude to the author who has given so much time and thought to this book. With the co-operation of Dr Fritz Heinrich, a former pupil and teacher of English and physical education, Dr Streicher has clarified points in the translation and organized the bibliography.

My thanks are due to the translator, Mrs C. R. M. Larner, who produced a clear and literal translation of the many essays selected from the original volumes. Her version forms the basis on which I worked: with the approval of Dr Streicher much has been altered since in the hope of making the text more accessible to the English reader and I take full responsibility for the final version. Mrs Larner showed a keen personal interest in the subject, which she related to the development of her own children, and her co-operation increased my own pleasure in the task.

I am very grateful to Mr R. St G. T. Harper, Director of the Department of Physical Education at the University of Manchester, for his constant support and for his advice on the presentation of the material; to Miss Jean Morley, Principal Lecturer and Head of the Department of Physical Education at Manchester College of Education, and to Mrs Ann Lewis, sometime Lecturer in Physical Education at the University of Wales, for their valuable and stimulating criticism of the manuscript; Mrs Lewis also helped to clarify some points in the translation and translated, for my benefit, a number of articles giving biographical details about Dr Gaulhofer and Dr Streicher.

Finally, I wish to express my sincere thanks to Mr T. L. Jones of the Manchester University Press for his continual assistance throughout the period of preparation of the manuscript, and to Miss Margaret L. M. Young who has had to live with the book for so many years and has helped me with many of the editorial problems.

Acknowledgements are due to Verlag für Jugend und Volk, Vienna; to Mrs Poldi Heinrich who renewed the drawings; to the Headmaster and children of St Clement's Primary School, Ardwick, Manchester who posed so patiently for the photograph for Plate I and finally to the trustees of the Dorette Wilkie Fund of Chelsea College of Physical Education for money to pay for a considerable part of the translation.

B.E.S.

Section I

The theory of movement

1   *The spectrum of movement and the place of physical education in it*

The term 'physical education' means the principle of the indivisible unit 'man' in the education of whom the body may be the point of attack but never the goal, this always being the whole man. Hence, consideration of human movement, that is of a much larger field than physical education can ever be, is of importance when determining the choice and arrangement of the exercises. Exercises, organized according to an educational purpose, constitute only a small part of the movements carried out by a person in his daily life. Movements beyond a certain level act as a stimulus to the organism; daily life, work and play provide such a stimulus, and this is what concerns us. One cannot devise a system of physical training as if only the exercises, arranged consciously and to a plan, exerted stimuli, nor as if only these exerted beneficial stimuli and life itself merely useless ones. The connection between the range of movements in life and in gymnastics must be seen clearly and without prejudice, otherwise too much or too little is expected of physical education.

The question therefore arises whether the same movements should be made in gymnastics as in daily life, or different ones, or whether both are necessary.

First we will forget about gymnastics and consider people with a very primitive way of life. They can preserve their lives only by moving: procuring food, making clothing and dwellings, keeping off enemies, propagating and bringing up children, and in addition taking part in festivals and celebrations; everything happens by means of movements of various kinds. To consider one example, locomotion; whether hunting or fleeing or going about daily affairs, the method of locomotion always depends on external conditions; many kinds of movement forwards are necessary and possible according to the terrain: whether mountains, cliffs, meadows, forest, water, etc. For us nowadays walking is the most common way of moving forwards but in the human apparatus of movement, climbing and mounting, swimming, crawling, sliding, slipping through, jumping over, etc., are as well provided for as walking. In primitive conditions they are necessary for life, and only when roads and paths run through the whole world and machine power can quickly carry us anywhere will all the other ways of moving forwards become more or less superfluous and their purpose forgotten.

Although walking and running, running and jumping, walking and mounting, are often so intertwined that it is not easy to define where they begin or end, they are so clearly recognizable as definite forms amongst the rest of human movement that in speech they have special names. These names tell us the purpose of the movement but say nothing about the way that trunk and limbs change position in it. These names are generally comprehensible. Even if one knows nothing about bones, muscles and nerves, one understands immediately what is meant by the word running. A person who wants to run does not need to be told which muscles he should contract. Such movements, characterized by their purpose, are the smallest units of movement, in a sense similar to that of the cell in the organism. These movements are called functional activities (see glossary) and are not only to be found in human locomotion but also where man has to deal with objects. As well as walking, running, jumping, mounting, climbing, etc., there is a clearly defined second group: pulling and pushing, lifting, carrying, and throwing. Here too the essence of the movement lies in the purpose of the functional activity; the goal is 'outside'.

External aids are not necessary for the execution of a functional activity; man needs only his own body. Nevertheless, man has invented external aids on a vast scale; the ladder, for example, was invented to make it easier to climb up something; a pole is used when vaulting and a basket when carrying. These in turn give rise to many new forms of movement, which are all founded on the original functional activity. Take 'sliding' as an example: sliding is in itself possible to man to a limited extent, but certain inventions such as skis and skates greatly enhance this potentiality, leading to special quite independent fields of activity which could not otherwise have been developed.

With the evolution of the tool, which is as characteristic of man as speech and walking upright, many new skills became part of man's movement repertoire. The improvement of tools and the invention of even better ones run parallel with advances in their skilful use.

The following consideration shows very clearly that this is not an imaginary idea but an actual process: the handling of tools often demands different work from each hand. The central regulator of the skeletal muscles is the cerebellum. In all mammals a distinction is made between the palaeocerebellum and the neocerebellum. There are some creatures which can use their limbs only in pairs, and they are capable of running, jumping, lying down, standing up, etc.; others can use each of their limbs independently of one another. The two extremes are cattle and man. The first group has a powerfully developed palaeocerebellum, in the second the neocerebellum predominates* (see Braus and Elze, 1932).

The biologically and culturally old functional activities are of special importance for physical education, for they exert adequate stimuli for man's apparatus of movement, as swimming does for fish and flying does for birds.

These functional activities form an essential and indispensable constituent of the exercise material of physical education and may be termed 'basic exercises'.

Biologically sound movement training must provide a varied experience of movement. The richness of form lent to each individual functional activity by the external circumstances of the natural sphere of the movement must be exploited in the training. This means that one must run uphill and downhill on various surfaces, must really experience the necessity for braking and accelerating, sudden twists and halts. No intentional arbitrarily willed leaning forwards or backwards can replace the change of position of the body as the inclination of the ground changes.

Teachers of physical education in general do not understand clearly enough how complicated is the process of a voluntary movement. Many teachers know that impulses go from the cerebrum to the motor root cells by means of the pyramidal tract, and from there to the muscles; but teachers of physical education often do not know that impulses are always passing over the cerebellum and the extrapyramidal tracts, and that even if the pyramidal tracts are intact, no regulated movement can occur without these impulses. Pathology proves this conclusively:

* Modern neuro-physiology leads to the realization that there are complicated feedback mechanisms involving much larger portions of the central nervous system.

for example, if the cerebellum is diseased there are characteristic disturbances of the movement; the impulses which run along the pyramidal tracts cannot assure co-ordinated movement on their own. Too little attention is usually paid to the reflex components which are localized in the evolutionally older parts of the brain and which are of such importance for retaining balance and correct muscle tone.

The steering of movement by the senses is also usually underestimated. Optical, acoustical, and tactile feelings are always being knitted into movement. If we lift an object which we wrongly thought would be heavy we experience how the feeling resulting from the movement modifies its further course.

The preservation of equilibrium in the body happens unconsciously; for example, no one can say how trunk, arms and legs must lie in relation to one another in order to regain balance after a landing. Nature has carefully entrusted this achievement to the phylogenetically old and therefore unfailingly sure parts of the nervous system. These also function in animals. When new gains are made by man he does not lose the earlier ones but they are overlaid and changed by the new ones.

In a functional movement, therefore, the attention is directed to a particular goal and not all the details of the movements are willed or noticed. Preserving equilibrium occurs mainly by means of reflexes. This reflex 'mechanism' must be allowed to take its course. If all the details of a movement are laid down by the teacher there is a danger of working against the reflexes. A sounding-lead levels off into its position of equilibrium. The limbs too reach the position of equilibrium if the joints are allowed 'free play'. This 'moving in equilibrium' is not learned from static work but only by having the courage repeatedly to lose one's balance and find it again.

Up to the present we have only dealt with purposeful movements but the variety of human movement is not increased only by the invention of new tools; there is another, very different, development which will now be considered.

People have enjoyed themselves since ancient times with movement. In games and sports they carry out movements which they also do seriously in their daily lives; they fight with one another in play, and they represent in heightened form the work to which they owe their livelihood. In this play they often ring

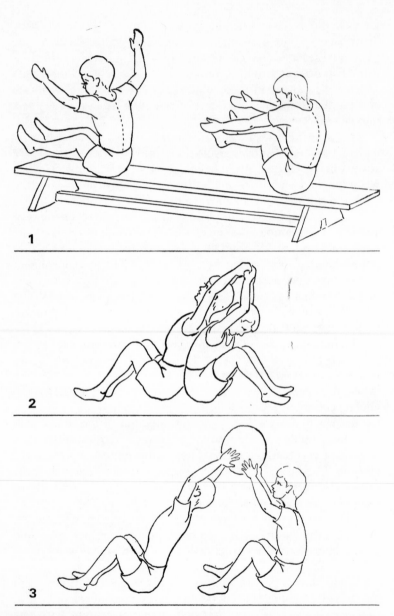

Figure 1. Swinging the legs over whilst sitting : compare the two backs
Figures 2 & 3. Stretching the pectoral spine in a position which restricts
movement

the changes on the functional activities. They enjoy the charm of the sound and the rhythm of the movement; they invent toys and develop new movements around them—which would not have been possible without these toys—just as they do around their tools in work. They take pleasure in doing more and more difficult things, and enjoy their ability when they are successful. There are countless examples of this, dating from the earliest times. With every functional activity a whole series of arts is connected in a gradation which can only be understood historically, and which are infinitely varied and infinitely capable of expansion. Throwing, running and climbing have no definite order of precedence but the complicated art of juggling clearly stands at the end of a series which begins with the tricks with balls played by children. There are a great number of jumping tricks and they can be arranged in a sequence which begins with purposeful jumps and leads via many transitional stages to the difficult, artistic jumps of dancers. Somersaulting, which occurs in wrestling and riding, and simply represents a fall being broken by rolling over, gradually by long tradition develops into the floor work of agility exercises and tumbling. Gymnastic tricks on apparatus are also the product of an historically comprehensible evolution from swinging on the horizontal and parallel bars; the swinging up on to the bar is still purposeful, its intention being to get up somewhere. Figure skating grows gradually out of simple sliding on skates, in which changing direction, stopping, avoiding things, naturally prove necessary. There is an analogy to this development in the techniques of knitting, crocheting, lace-making, etc.; Brussels lace would be unthinkable without a long evolution leading up to it.

The law of the conservation of energy governs the functional activities when they appear as forms with a purpose because their meaning is 'work'; something is done which is necessary, or which can at least be considered necessary; but they also appear as art forms (see glossary) which have nothing to do with the necessities of life. If in doubt about distinguishing between them, imagine a situation in which there is danger to one's own or another's life. If a person, standing on the three-metre board about to do an elegant dive, suddenly sees a child go under, he will instantly jump into the water as quickly and accurately as possible.

The question arises, should the two groups of movements stemming from life itself, the purposeful and art forms, be used exclusively in well-constructed schemes of physical education, or should special movements which do not occur in life but are the result of educational theory be applied as well? Or should physical education consist only of the latter?

Before this question can be answered these forms, which do not occur in life but have their origins in the school, must be examined more closely.

On careful consideration it can be seen that these movements have been obtained by dissecting functional activities. Large or small parts have been taken out of the total movement and executed on their own. So, for example, the movement called 'knee-bending' is to be found in landing after a jump, but also in bending down and slipping through a gap. Raising the leg or knee occurs as a constituent of climbing, but also of walking and jumping. Raising the arm is a part of throwing, but also of lifting, carrying, and of standing and running jumps. It must be made clear that the 'whole comes before the parts'—that the functional activity was there before its parts had been recognized or given special names; the parts have actually been separated out from the whole. These movements, which have been obtained by dissecting functional activities and have no intellectual content of their own, are called partial movements (see glossary).

Partial movements are peculiar to physical education which is deliberately framed as a means of educating young people. They do not occur in everyday life; no child by himself, without being spurred on by an adult, practises swinging his leg or circling his trunk.

The question can now be put more precisely: should physical education consist only of purposeful and art forms, or should partial movements also be included, or should the latter form the total material?

In order to find an answer to this question we will first consider the two children in Figure 1. No one would dispute that the child on the left has a better back than the one on the right. Teachers of physical education will agree that the latter should do special corrective exercises, that just running about a lot is not enough for this child. If one compares Figure 2 with Figure 3 one sees that it is possible in various ways to make the child adopt a position, at least for a moment or two, which is good for his back. A primary schoolchild will be inclined to repeat the exercises because he finds them fun; the fact that they 'do him good' is of no importance to him. Nevertheless, the main reason for using partial movements lies in the fact of 'evasion'. Movements can be co-ordinated in very different ways and understandably and unconsciously every person chooses the way which is easiest for him. So weak places are usually bypassed. For example, if the thorax is inflexible bending usually takes place at the hips and bending in the thoracic region is avoided. However, it is in precisely such faults as appear in the child's back in Figure 1 that it is important for the movement to reach certain places. Usually this can be achieved only by starting off from a position which restricts movement in certain parts, in this example the hips, and leaves the other parts of the body free to move.

Another reason for using partial movements is to help in the teaching of the functional activities. This can be seen clearly in the teaching of swimming where, increasingly, partial movements are used so that swimming can be taught to many pupils at the same time more quickly and easily. For example, the pupils learning backstroke carry out the leg movements, at the same time just moving their arms slowly up and down. The purpose of this exercise is to enable the teacher to supervise the leg movements and so make sure that they are carried out firmly but with a minimum of tension. Nobody thinks that these exercises have any value on their own, they are good only if they improve the swimming. Nobody combines new exercises at will from these partial movements; they remain bound up with the process of learning to swim.

So, partial movements are indispensable but they must not outnumber the others, and they must not become independent. Above all, they must not be used as elements for permutations, variations, and combinations to increase the stock of exercises. This leads straight to unfunctional work.

To arrive at a satisfactory theory of human movement, one must first review all the relevant facts (there are extraordinarily many) and take into account the flexibility, versatility and the manifold different ways of doing things in work, at play, and at rest. To begin with no attempt is made at an evaluation. The kinds of work which deform people are ascertained with the same interest as those which further them physically. Also then, when physical exercise is consciously applied as a means of education, the usefulness of work and play is considered.

It becomes necessary to evaluate these activities biologically (the word 'biological' must be taken in a wide sense, not just as something purely physical) and to decide whether they apply profitable stimuli or not. The educationally valuable activities are chosen from the vast field of purposeful and art forms of movement. Also prescribed with the purposeful and art forms there is the stock of partial movements which has been built up by a long teaching tradition. They were obtained by analysing the functional activities and are used as a means of teaching and correcting these activities.

This theory of movement as a basis for physical education is not a question of improving methods but is concerned with the total question of movement training. The following four examples will show how this theory of movement works in practice.

(i) *The use of apparatus*. The most obvious difference between primitive man and those living in the artificial surroundings of a city is impoverishment in locomotion. Walking, climbing stairs, perhaps a little running, sitting or lying down, and standing up are the sum total of movement in daily life. However, a child needs the whole profusion of human locomotion, only this will give him all the stimuli necessary for growth. Even if all the physical education lessons could be held in the open this would not be enough, for the prepared games pitch also presents too few opportunities. In our climate indoor exercising inevitably plays a large role. Gymnastic apparatus is the means by which we can give the children, to a certain extent at least, variety of locomotion; they have not only the horizontal floor but can also move upwards and downwards; they can mount and climb, swing, rock, go hand over hand, and balance. So if someone lays down as a principle 'never to use apparatus' he is saying that he does not consider climbing necessary. The question of the use of apparatus solves itself as soon as it is considered from the right starting-point.

(ii) *Judging good and bad*. Early German gymnastics were characterized by 'jerky' movement. Some later gymnastic systems were characterized by swinging: which is better, to raise one's arm with control, with a swing, or with a jerk? Is it correct to carry out all movements with a swing? An answer cannot be given to this question, one way of moving can be as good or as bad as another. In partial movements one cannot discover a rule from the movement itself, whereas in functional activities judgement is made according to the goal to be achieved. When a person is placing a slide under the microscope a swinging movement would be impractical, it would not achieve the necessary precision in space, but in throwing it is correct to swing the arm. So in functional activities objective judgement is possible.

If somebody always fails when a movement depends on swinging, he is made to swing his arms, legs and body. He is reminded of a bell and his attention is drawn to the word swinging and its sound. Some of the pupils may join in the swinging movements together because this carries the individual along. It can take many lessons before an impeded person can really swing freely, and it takes even longer before he can build the swinging into the functional activities.

From observing the pupils in the functional activities one knows what must be practised, and one knows it only from such observation. And in order to find out if the lessons have helped the pupils, they must once more be observed in the functional activities.

(iii) *Correction.* The principle of 'finding the best solution for the individual' is often taken to mean 'never correcting anything'. This is not the case but nevertheless the method of correcting functional work is not direct and it is slow. The teacher must be patient as he knows that every functional activity improves by itself if it is carried out often enough in varying situations; he just has to wait for this self-improvement. Only when he sees that some faults are not disappearing on their own, or that new ones are actually appearing does the teacher need to take a hand. How does he intervene? He knows that in order to complete a jump over an obstacle successfully the landing must be resilient. He draws the attention of the pupil to this detail and tells him to concentrate on jumping in such a way that he cannot hear the landing. If the pupil does not succeed in doing this he makes him just jump up in order to land, or even climb up on something and land on the floor. Then the pupil has no other difficulty to contend with than the feeling of give in his legs. Once this has been learnt the jump is repeated over the obstacle.

(iv) *How should partial movements be used in the lesson?* An example is the exercise of bobbing up and down whilst standing in the water. Three teachers prescribe it. The first tells the pupils to stay under the water as long as possible and, praising the one who emerges last, he pricks their ambition. He takes a stop-watch and ascertains precise times. Gradually this becomes a competition between two leading pupils, then a national record, finally a world record.

The second goes about it quite differently. He gives all his attention to seeing that the exercise has the appearance of proceeding in beautiful order, ranks straight as a die, distance between the pupils exactly equal, etc. The spectators at the performance will doubtless be enthusiastic.

The third teacher tells the pupils that the point is not to stay under the water as long as possible but not to stop breathing; a gentle current of air must escape continually through the nose and this can be seen from the bubbles which ascend during the exercise. The pupils must supervise themselves carefully. Ambition to stay under as long as possible has no sense if the breath is held. The teacher will watch individual pupils very carefully and draw their attention to their faults. He has no time to work with his pupils for a regular and simultaneous perfor-mance. In an exhibition performance he would be at a disadvan-tage, nor can he compete with the first teacher. Nevertheless his pupils will thank him when they can swim effortlessly because they are breathing correctly—not only those who are well endowed by nature and have achieved it by themselves, but all of them.

These four examples should show how radically the approach is altered when one takes the functional activity as the basis for the performance of prescribed movements.

2 Gravity and natural movement

> One thing he must learn again: to fall, patiently resting in
> gravity. . . .
>
> Rilke, *Stundenbuch*

Physical education could well be described as applied biology, so
it is not to be wondered at that a similar course of development
is to be seen in both.

The great upswing of science in the second half of the last
century resulted in an immoderate presumption on the part of
man, clearly expressed in the slogan of 'man's dominion over
nature'. All questions were thought to be answerable, all forces
manageable, just because man had been successful in fathoming
several natural laws in quick succession which had up to then
been hidden. We are now able to see a retreat from this attitude—
more and more there is a modest bearing towards nature; we know
that behind every puzzle solved by science another one appears.

The same change of attitude is to be felt in gymnastics. The
unacceptable aspect of many methods of gymnastics, the disre-
garding of the inner demands of the body and the carrying
through by force of demands from outside, date without exception from the time of 'man's dominion over nature'. The modern
approach involves a completely different attitude to the body:
the human body is now considered one of the miracles of nature,
whose laws must be discovered, for in them is recognized the
basis of all educational work. From such an attitude a quite
different form of gymnastics is bound to grow than from that of
desiring to subjugate the body to the mind.

This was of course the reason why the arguments in support
of the old and the new gymnastics were so virulent; in the final
analysis it is a question of different outlooks on life, which, here
as in other fields, clash with one another.

The demand made again and again for natural movement is
only an expression of the search for the new foundations which
the body itself can provide. Moving naturally means nothing
other than moving according to the laws of the body. It is a
manner of working, not a particular group of movements—not
even those necessary for maintenance of life. Whether one tills

the ground or stands at a machine in a workshop where there is
extensive division of labour, whether one plays, hikes, or swims,
or whether one exercises in a gymnasium, movements can
always be natural. In physical education, for various reasons,
movements must also be used which never happen in everyday
life, such as vaulting and agility exercises and partial movements,
but these too must be carried out naturally.

It is not at all easy to put into words what is meant by natural;
least of all does it help to substitute the word 'rhythmic' for
'natural', for 'rhythm' is shot through with all sorts of possible
meanings.

By concentrating on a sympathetic observation of animals and
of children untouched by education, people of a predominantly
artistic bent can come to a recognition of natural movement.
However, this path is not open to all people. For the more
intellectual person one must try to indicate the characteristics of
natural movement by explaining the mechanical conditioning
factors (see Steinemann, 1924).

The following is an attempt to analyse what seem to be the
essential distinguishing qualities of natural movement.

Gymnastics (in the widest sense) have been called a game
with gravity. On a little reflection one will find this image justified. All walking and running is a progression of the weight of
one's own body; every swinging up of the body on to something,
every vault, demands the lifting of one's own weight.

This battle with gravity is universally familiar but one can
add to it quite another consideration, and only this fully explores
the meaning of the phrase 'game with gravity'. Our body is an
articulate structure; its parts can be moved in opposite directions, can adopt various positions, with regard to one another,
and in space. In this the force of gravity is of decisive importance.
To make this clear a few basic facts of the theory of movement
must be given.

The bones have been compared with lever arms moved by
muscles. Every muscle spans at least one joint and is therefore
joined to two different bones. One end is named the origin, the
other the insertion, and it is usually imagined that when the
muscle is contracted the insertion approaches the origin which
does not move.

This is not quite correct: the origin and the insertion both move, both bones adjacent to the muscle change their position. The general opinion would only be correct if one of the bones were somehow rigidly fixed but this is not usually the case.

Braus gives in his *Anatomy of Man* (1921) the following very illuminating image:

When one holds an open pocket-knife in the air by the tip of the blade, the handle representing one bone and the blade the other, it is exactly perpendicular. When one shuts the blade slowly the knife is displaced until it is in equilibrium, the handle deviates to one side and the blade to the other. The same thing happens in the bones. The displacement of both parts continues until the centre of gravity lies under the point of suspension.

It would naturally be of interest, and is quite possible, to ascertain mathematically a relationship between the angle made by the blade with the handle and the deviation of the blade from the perpendicular. For ordinary life it is enough to retain this angle by allowing the force of gravity to take effect; like a sounding-lead the penknife levels out into the 'correct' position. Indeed, it is scarcely to be doubted that any computation would be inferior to reality in precision—such sums usually do not work out exactly—and above all it would be of no practical use. Otherwise, when the most precise adjustment is needed, man would not always merely allow gravity to take effect as in the scales, the hydrostatic balance, the plumb-line; however delicate such instruments may be, the basis for them is always the allowing of the force of gravity to bring about a state of equilibrium.

These instruments, in comparison with the human body, are simple. It would scarcely be possible to calculate movements or to analyse how power takes effect in a joint system consisting of so many joints. As we know, theoretical mechanics has no possibility of doing this (Haglund, 1923).

Braus (1921) also shows that this reflection on the freely swinging penknife can be applied to the arm as well. In changing from a stretched to a bent position the displacement of the upper and lower arm continues until the centre of gravity lies under the point of suspension. In general the muscles work from both ends as they seek to bring the two parts of the skeleton to which they are attached closer together. . . . The displacement of the two parts always continues to a point where the centre of gravity lies immediately below the point of suspension (or above the

fulcrum, Streicher). Tracing the derivation of bodily movements
from the displacement of the centres of gravity of separate masses
moving in relation to each other is the basis of the mechanics of
movement.

It seems to be a characteristic of unnatural movement that the
remote effect is impeded; neighbouring joints are not allowed
the free play which would permit the movement to continue in
them and swing through them, but are held rigid. By using
muscular force, the upper arm can be held in the position it had
when the arm was hanging straight down (see Figure 4). Then
the arm does not level out into a new position of equilibrium;
the movement has been done unnaturally. It must be immediately
obvious that more strength is needed for this method of execution than when the arm is allowed to level out.

Perhaps somebody will here object that the purpose of
gymnastics is to strengthen the muscles, and that it is therefore
not at all correct to eliminate a form of muscular work. Although
this objection is ill-founded we will try, by yet more detailed
dissection of the example of bending the arm, to show how and
why the artificial execution is wrong.

The muscles which bend the arm determine by their contraction the relative position of upper and lower arm. Whether the
angle between them is large or small depends, mechanically, on
the degree of contraction of the muscle or, seen in another way,
on the purpose of the movement. The image of the lever does
not tell us which position in space the arm will adopt when it
is bent more, or less. That is quite another question, and one
which is too seldom clearly enough distinguished from the first.

The usual impression of the lever effect refers to what happens in the elbow joint. This remains the same no matter
whether the movement is carried out naturally or unnaturally.

In contrast to this the action of levelling out, which we have
already decided is necessary for natural movement, takes place
in the shoulder joint.

The arm does not hover freely in space but is attached to the
body at the shoulder. When no other muscles are working the
arm levels out like a lead under the influence of gravity into a
position of equilibrium. If one impedes this by muscular contraction, the desire of the arm to reach the position of equilibrium
still remains; it expresses itself as a tug which the muscles resist,

and so they are tense. In some circumstances this can be very significant—for example, when a stone is held up in order to let it suddenly crash down. The impetus of the arm falling will greatly strengthen the effect of the muscles pulling the arm down, and a person who wants to hit hard will not overlook the following effect: that the arm, when it is raised out of a position of equilibrium, tries to return to it, and that pressure against something preventing it from doing so can be utilized as 'strength'. This is the thought behind the weight theory of piano technique (Breithaupt, 1921).

Remaining tense can also be completely senseless. One does not continue to hold a stone in the air with no purpose. When there is no reason for work to be done by the muscles they must be allowed to rest and recuperate. In our example they can do this only when the arm is in its position of equilibrium. This saves them so that, when needed, they will be able to work harder.

Now one can also see the reason why a natural movement never stops suddenly with a jerk but levels out, ebbs; a position of equilibrium cannot be attained in any other way.

Avoiding spasmodic tension is not only of importance for the resting position once it has been reached; during the movement too, especially in the muscles not directly engaged, all immoderate tension must be avoided since otherwise control of the movement by the distribution of mass is ruled out. It would, of course, be quite wrong to bend the arm with the upper part of it held rigid, and afterwards allow it to level out. Whilst the arm is being bent the movement is controlled not only by the muscles but by the force of gravity as well; the whole course of the movement, not just the final position, takes place differently in the natural, as against the artificial, execution of it.

All these relationships are easier to see and describe in our arms, long levers hanging free as the extremities of the great lever system of our body, than in the trunk with its countless short levers, making only tiny oscillations. This is why we chose arm bending as our example.

Up to now we have assumed that only the muscles of the elbow are active, all the others at rest, so that movement gets weaker and weaker as it gets further from the point of departure, until it finally stops; but it can also happen that the muscles of the shoulder take part because this is demanded by the purpose of the movement. The observations made earlier still hold good, only the point of suspension of the sounding-lead in question would be displaced inwards to the next joint, and it would no longer consist of two parts (if one neglects the hand) but of three.

In other words we are taking the step, necessary even before this, of extending our reflections to the whole lever system of the body instead of, as up to now, considering one of its extremities.

For the shoulder girdle on which the arms hang the image of the sounding-lead is no longer appropriate, for it does not hang but is supported. It must be replaced by the image of a pair of scales. One can see at once that remaining in equilibrium, and the determinative influence of the distribution of mass, are just as important here as before. We can go straight on—since it would take too long to go through all the intermediate steps— to say that the whole body can be conceived as a pair of scales. As the scale-beam, supported from underneath, rests in equilibrium, so the trunk, resting on the legs in the two hip-joints, is held in swaying equilibrium.

Of course, man has an ability to move himself which the scales do not possess, but this does not raise him above the necessity of continually trying to reach a position of equilibrium. He can seek any position of equilibrium he will, or he can change it as often as he likes, but he cannot be quite without equilibrium. His freedom lies within this given state.

Certainly this comparison with a pair of scales does not completely explain the difficult question of human movement, for the scales would only respond to an outside influence such as being weighted or shaken; they are not active of their own accord. The fact that man has the ability to initiate movement himself is completely set aside when one compares the body to a pair of scales, but the more familiar comparison of the bones with lever arms is just as one-sided.

From the point of view of physics scales too are a lever; but from the point of view of their function they are completely different. A lever is a machine for altering the direction, working point, or power of a force; scales are an instrument for indicating something.

The comparison of the bones with lever arms recognizes only

their ability to move of their own accord. It fails by taking too little account of the weight of the lever arms and the fact that they are fastened to something, their connection with those adjacent to them, and their position in space. It is not simply a case of mathematical levers which, hovering in space, can adopt any position they choose, completely ignoring gravity as a directional force. How can a system of levers, supported only at two points and in unstable equilibrium, be determined in its position in space other than by the distribution of mass, that is by gravity?

Neither of the two images, lever and scales, invalidates the other. Both are justified, since both do justice to one side of human movement; indeed both are necessary because one is incomplete without the other.

It is understandable that people who considered themselves absolute rulers over nature overvalued the fact that man is able to move his own body, whilst forgetting that his movements are determined by gravity. We do possess the ability to move as we wish but this does not mean that we have escaped from the general forces to which everything on earth is subject. The sensible course is to try to make use of these forces. If adjustment into the greater whole of the natural forces is lost, free-will turns to arbitrariness.

When a person has forgotten how to let his movements be regulated by gravity, that is by the distribution of mass, as well as by the pull of his muscles, he must first relearn in isolation to allow gravity to take effect without disturbing the course of the movement with arbitrary muscular effort.

> This is the aim of all falling exercises such as: leaning as far as possible forwards in a standing position, and then checking the otherwise unavoidable fall with a few steps.
>
> Falling exercises loosen over-tension, and the conscious abandoning of oneself to gravity makes the levelling out into the new position of equilibrium easier.
>
> With these exercises, more easily than with others, one learns to feel how the course of a movement is determined by the distribution of mass.

For those who might be anxious about them for reasons of safety, we expressly state that falling and tumbling is not a goal of gymnastics but a means to awaken the slumbering feeling for the weight of each individual part of the body; a means which, like the exercises in flexibility, must be ended as soon as its purpose has been attained.

Without a delicate, ever-waking feeling for gravity no one can grow out of personal arbitrariness of movement; training in it is thus an indispensable prerequisite of all advanced physical education. How this training can be instigated is a question of method which is reserved for separate discussion. This much we will say here, that it is not something purely physical; anyone who cannot bring his pupils confidently to allow themselves to be carried by the natural forces will achieve nothing. This can only be done by a teacher who has experienced inside himself the change mentioned at the beginning, who has found the poet's phrase of 'resting in gravity' to be the truth.

Here these reflections close. Natural movement seems to be that which is controlled not only by the powers of the body, the power of the muscles, but also by the force of gravity, always and everywhere present. This wonderful interplay of the two forces in all movements has definite laws which must always be taken into consideration.

For the teacher of physical education then, the expression 'natural movement' means a method of work, not a group of movements limited in any way. It is an essential distinguishing feature of 'natural movement' that it leads from one position of equilibrium into another, and that it is, throughout its course, determined not only by the pull of the muscles and the control of the joint-surfaces, but also by the distribution of mass in the body.

3 Good form in movement

In every subject special concepts develop with varying degrees of precision in their definition. It is often a certain speech usage as, for example, in the expression 'movement training', which is nowadays on everyone's lips, without there being any agreement as to its true meaning. This technical vocabulary can suddenly become inadequate, as, for example, when the subject is classified according to a new system of reference. So it is in the question of form in movement. Our ideas have radically changed. They have been deeply influenced by the evolution of athletics, by organized games and by modern gymnastics; the pathology of movement has also added to our knowledge, just as important stimuli have come from neurology and Gestalt psychology (Krueger and Klemm, 1933)—to name only a few of the most important influences. The rigid form which governed gymnastics in the nineteenth century collapsed, and with it the vocabulary in which it was taught became obsolete, too. The new vocabulary, although by no means a uniform one, has developed at least to the point of providing clarification of working problems; but a new vocabulary is not enough. One must from time to time review the theory and provide a comprehensive theoretical reinterpretation; the expressions employed in the need of the moment must be carefully tested and refined, otherwise with vague words vague ideas creep into the practical work.

Nowadays we see so much more than before in movement that we must thoroughly investigate the whole question. How should movements be executed, and when is their form considered good? To learn to see good form in movement, what we have accepted as normal—mere tradition, style, and fashion—must be put aside. A universally valid basis must be found from which we can educate. Unprejudiced, sympathetic observation of the wonderful structure of the human body and its movements as a phenomenon in space and time, allows people to recognize that the laws of form are just as reliable guides as biological laws.

Spitzy (1914), discussing posture education, pointed out that every structure must be 'right', both in bearing down and in supporting, otherwise it collapses; and this is true of every structure, whatever the manner in which it is built. Other considerations such as style, grace, etc., mask, one might say, its conformity with the laws of statics. They hide these laws but cannot evade them. The laws remain valid however the structure may finally appear to the eye.

How can this uncommitted, this ever-present basis of movement which will make us independent of changing human concepts of beauty be found? Theoretically, one could say that this is a question of fidelity to biological laws, but what does the biologically correct look like, and how can it be represented so that it may become of use for practical work?

Firstly, as a phenomenon in space every movement has to start somewhere. The point of attack of a movement should, as Kleist indicated in his essay 'On the Marionette Theatre' (1810), be the body's centre of gravity. Many people unconsciously follow this principle when doing physical work; occasionally one can observe it beautifully exemplified in peasants or workers. From the centre of gravity the movement runs outwards; it is centrifugal; in, for example, movements of the limbs it always begins in the part nearest the trunk. The centrifugal movement must be taken as far as possible outwards, so that it becomes large and spacious instead of being small and cramped into the body; it must grow into the surrounding space. Here the long-familiar importance of taking pleasure in physical exercise is illuminated from another side; according to Klages (1921) it increases the desire to move and thus works directly to further large movements.

Secondly, how the movements which come from the centre of gravity run through the lever system of the human body depends on the interplay of the joints and the co-ordination of the muscles, and so is not determined by the will but follows laws. However, one must not think that human movements can be entirely explained mechanically; otherwise we would not be able to recognize a person by his movements. The body does not work like a machine. In the last analysis it is not mechanical factors such as the form of the surfaces of the joints, the ligaments, etc., that determine the course of the movements. The mechanical prerequisites provide only the possibilities; the movements that actually take place at any given time are determined by the nervous system, which directs the immensely complicated play of the muscles.

Thirdly, we will discuss position in space, which is determined by gravity. The body is always under the influence of gravity. In water-animals and in plants its directional pull is recognized. The human body—by the structure of its parts, their relationship to each other and the way they are 'built up' one part on another —is held upright, with the minimum of muscular effort, against gravity; it 'rests in gravity'.

Comprehension of a movement as a spatial phenomenon is helped by calling the pupils' attention to special traits as, for example, where the movement begins, where it ends, through which joints it passes, to what extent the joints participate in the movement, etc.

Another group of laws of form results from the course of the movements in time, and the amount of strength used. An important criterion for judging good or bad execution is the conservation of energy.

Every human movement is brought about by muscular activity but once the work has been done, muscles must return to their natural state of lack of tension. It is wrong, after a jump or swinging off a piece of apparatus, to stand with muscles tensed, for now the work has been done and in order to stand upright only very delicate muscular play is necessary, of which we are not normally conscious but which can be gathered from the increased rate of breathing when standing compared with lying.

So every movement rises like a wave from the position of rest and sinks back into it; stopping at any point would interfere with the wave movement, for the essence of waves is continual motion. One must allow every wave of movement to come to an end, must not prematurely impede it; this results in delicate bouncing and swinging away which must not be destroyed by exercising stiffly to a beat, or with a rigid posture. How high the wave climbs depends on the goal and purpose of the movement. Strict attention must be paid to seeing that the energy used is appropriate to the task to be fulfilled; it is wrong to jump over a low rope with enormous take-off and impetus. This law is, of course, only another expression of the familiar demand to work economically.

Just as the height of a wave is closely dependent on the purpose of the movement, so is its span. Executing a movement of wide span takes longer than executing a narrow one; a gentle turn of the head gives a different movement wave from lifting a heavy object. So movements of trunk and limbs cannot be coupled into groups of exercises to be done rhythmically with reference to factors solely outside the body.

The image of the wave for the course of a movement in time originates from the breathing which floods ceaselessly through the living body, at one time rising and falling regularly in long, flat waves, at another towering into high waves in working or exercising. Movements comprehended by the image of a wave do not disturb the breathing, itself a mobile, ever-changing wave; it is disturbed only by interruption or fixing.

The laws of movement in time are followed as long as one conceives all movements as waves traversing the body.

Swimming, skating and skiing, throwing, running and jumping, follow these laws of form in space and time; gymnastics, in the form of tricks on apparatus, still often resists these laws out of a quite unjustified fear of lessening achievement.

However, once one has recognized that these laws are general laws for all movement whether work, exercise, everyday movement, artistic technique, or physical representation, one must also apply them to all forms of gymnastics; and then it is no longer a question of which exercises are done but of how they are done if their execution is to be biologically correct.

The functional activities (see glossary), as has already been stated, form the basis of movement. It is part of their essence to have a shape and this shape is not imposed on them by man. These activities are recognizable by the form peculiar to them, which makes them stand out against the generality of human movement like shapes in silhouette. They must be referred to if one wishes to be clear about the question of form in movement.

One notices it perhaps only in passing but it is a strange thought that so many exercises are described by nouns, e.g. a jump—yet here lies the key to important perceptions. How are these nouns related to the verbs that describe the functional activities? Which comes first, the noun or the verb? How is one developed from the other?

Every functional activity is a form capable of variation. It represents no stereotyped course of movement—and yet the form is always recognizable. The functional activity remains itself even under quite different outer—and even inner—circumstances. For every functional activity is essentially the coming to terms of a living being with its surroundings; thus it is firmly bound to the situation, and is determined as much by the living organism as by the surroundings. Without the variability peculiar to it this would be impossible. How could we find our step on uneven ground if the length of our stride were not variable? How differently we place our feet when we do not wish to be heard, or when we walk firmly along the paths between the flower-beds in a garden. We walk quite differently when uplifted by joy, or when depressed by sorrow.

Without the variability inherent in them, functional activities could not articulate with one another, or with other movements either, as, for example, with movements of expression, or with fragmentary ones, that is movements which are begun but not completed. Functional activities never stand alone in the stream of life; they reach at once into the past and into the future. The movements in our life form an uninterrupted stream which is only broken by sleep—and even then not completely.

One must thus grasp that functional activities are definite, well-characterized forms of movement that are capable of variation.

There are formal characteristics which reappear in all the various aspects of one functional activity. Not just one definite form of walking, e.g. on level ground, is called good. It is possible to walk well or badly downhill or uphill, loaded or unloaded. Swimming can be good in still as in running water, and climbing on a difficult or an easy path. That which is necessary for this functional activity in all the changing outer circumstances constitutes its good form, the 'conditioning law of its structure'. This we must seek.

As an example we will take swimming. No detailed explanation is necessary to show that only the horizontal position is suitable for producing the most long-lasting movement forward in the water. Since every corner on the gliding surface magnifies the resistance to the water, complete extension is necessary; it must not, however, lead to rigidity, for then the breathing would suffer. Arm and leg movements must serve only to further progress and not to try to keep oneself up. Besides this the body must be controlled so that it becomes as slim and pointed as possible to reduce the water resistance to a minimum. In so doing one must let oneself be elongated by the water, the body must be held in the stretched position given it by the water—and then it is balanced like a plank which has been thrown into the water. If the effort is conscious however, it is no easier to find one's balance in the water than to restore it after jumping from a height. The limbs must alternate between 'tense' and 'supple' in their movements to and fro, in order now to utilize the resistance of the water, now to avoid it. The impulses from the arm and leg movements must interact properly; before one has finished gliding forward one must speed oneself up again, for it is more difficult to set a standing vehicle in motion than to increase the pace of one that is already moving. And finally, the movements must be in harmony with the breathing, otherwise one cannot swim for any length of time.

These requirements must be fulfilled in every type of swimming. They can also be attained for any type of swimming, and always before any specific technique is taught. Everything which has here had to be set down consecutively must then occur at one and the same time, only in this way can the inner regulation of the activity of swimming which we call its good form, result.

Good form builds itself up gradually quite by itself if a person has the time and peace to come to terms with the water. Functional activities have the ability to correct themselves. The fact that feeling and movement mutually qualify one another is grounded in the human organism. The situation makes its own demands, or rather, the human being, in his coming to terms with his surroundings, has to do it in a certain way. He is regulated to fit in with his surroundings and so they direct him, force him to do it thus and in no other way. In these determinations of form there is therefore no element of will.

We must therefore learn to see good form in the 'forms' which have not yet been objectivized. In the objectivized 'forms' one cannot be sure whether they have been determined by 'nature' or by 'culture', that is, by human intervention. What then does objectivized mean? It is clearly put by Wundt (1907):

Speech always fixes a transitory event in a lasting expression. Even when it at first allows one to recognize events and states in their true meaning by making use of verbal forms, it gradually attempts to form substantives, which change the event into a permanent concept for the sake of abstract thought. Instead of remaining conscious of this origin of our concepts we tend to transfer the changed form to the objective happening itself. By converting the variable phenomenon into an unchangeable concept, and the latter into a word used as a noun, the fleeting event itself seems to become a relatively permanent object. What has reality only as a happening and an action finally becomes something which itself has qualities.

The following example may help to clarify the argument. The transitory event, the variable phenomenon, could perhaps be represented by the cry: 'Look, the boy is jumping over the fence!' The fence is just over waist high, the boy has a whip in one hand; he runs up and takes a running jump, just touching the fence with his free hand, and runs on. The objectivized 'form' is the 'fence vault', it has thus a name which has only one meaning. The objectivized 'form' can be repeated at any time, whereas the functional activity, being dependent on circumstance, is, strictly speaking, unrepeatable. Given certain external presuppositions, such as something over which one can do a 'fence vault' (type and kind of obstacle, take-off and landing place, etc.) one can carry out this special kind of jumping, that is, this vault. It has special peculiarities, like an object; if the 'fence vault' is done differently it is no longer a 'fence vault'.

The occurrence of objectivization takes place especially when a system of instruction is developed, when planned activity begins, which presupposes completeness and order. This is the case in the realm of movement when 'domestic natural gymnastics' (Pestalozzi, 1807) are succeeded by 'artificial gymnastics' where teaching schedules demand generally comprehensible descriptions for exercises. Hence the many nouns in our stock of exercises!

Thus, objectivization goes hand in hand with a definition of 'jumping method' and we can really only now speak of definite 'forms'. Among these, are forms determined by the human mind. For example, in a somersault one is supposed to remain true to the axis: that is, with complete symmetry. If somebody were to fall from the horse he was riding one would not consider it incorrect if he were to break his fall by rolling over one shoulder.

Our human striving for generality, for regularity, order, etc., can thus serve us in bad stead. The mere work of humans comes to have the status of natural laws. Once you allow yourself to depart too far from the real situation you can impose all sorts of unnatural directions which have no warrant in biological laws. Individual points are emphasized, underlined and made prominent; these may well be present in reality but they are there limited and controlled by other factors. One is free from all ties as soon as one steps out of the 'circle of necessity', as soon as one more or less frees oneself from the real situation. Then one factor can be greatly emphasized at the expense of others, for example, the height of a jump, by taking a symbolical obstacle in the form of a rope or a pole and developing a special technique. To give another example: if on a skiing trip one skier falls and breaks a leg his companion will fetch help as quickly as possible—but his speed will be limited by the necessity for safety, otherwise both will end up lying helpless in the snow. Whereas in organized racing the competitors can go as fast as possible, for an ambulance will probably be standing by and in case of need can reach the hospital very quickly.

All this means that the exercises of physical education which are expressed by nouns have got a natural form—but men have overlaid it with their own conception of form. It is difficult to recognize from these exercises what their natural good form is, as it is mixed with arbitrary precepts and with technique. One must refer back to the variable original functional activity described by the verb, which is strictly and unconditionally tied up with a real situation. By comparing these two, one can gradually learn to differentiate between the natural and artificial elements in the objectivized forms. That the former are more important than the latter is easy to see and is daily confirmed by practical work.

*The movement task and its
      contribution to good form*

The term movement task has been used in very different, indeed almost contradictory, senses by the exponents of various gymnastic systems and in contrast to the clearly and sharply defined concepts of the system worked out by Gaulhofer (and Streicher, 1930). Despite this the term has become generally accepted and has done good service in practical work. So in the 'handling of the concept' a clear enough image of what it means must have developed. To find out what this image was the author asked various physical activity groups each to note down three examples of movement tasks: one from the field of swimming, one from skiing, and one from the work done either in the gymnasium or on the games pitch or in the countryside.

Examining these examples showed that some had to be eliminated immediately because they were obviously based on some misconception—e.g. catching games. Others had to be excluded because they would have made the term movement task such a general concept that it would have had no more meaning as a technical term—examples of this are: jumping up at a branch, fetching a plate from the bottom of the water, climbing over an obstacle. Were one to call these exercises movement tasks the term would mean tasks accomplished by movement, but the physical education teacher sets no other kind of task; it would be a distinction only from tasks not solved by movement.

Exercises described by a definite name, such as somersaults, cartwheels, forward rolls, side vaults, front vaults, rear vaults, were also excluded.

Now only the 'debatable' examples are left; from them the characterization must be drawn.

One thing is clear: the movement task is something invented by the teacher. Tasks which life itself could set, such as climbing a tree, throwing a stone at fruit on a tree, jumping over a stream, climbing over a fence, pushing a box away, are not movement tasks. In these cases the course of the movement is entirely determined by external conditions together with the inner state of the person doing it. The individual shape of the tree presents certain handholds and footholds of which the climber makes use; one can jump over the stream just here because its width lies within one's jumping capacity, and because a suitable landing place beckons on the other side of the water. Every such jump is unique and unrepeatable; one may come to the same place again next day but it has rained in the night, the ground is damp and slippery, or one is carrying a burden one did not have the day before; at the very least one has jumped over this stream yesterday so today's jump no longer gives one the experience of doing it 'for the first time'.

So in these purely purposeful forms the situation decides everything and the teacher nothing. If he wishes to make use of them when working with his pupils all he has to do is look out for these situations or create them; but then he asks only that they be overcome somehow, each pupil remains free to choose how.

In this kind of situation one can recognize that teaching and learning are general human relationships and cannot be narrowed down to the teacher-pupil relationship. For if such a situation occurs in everyday life and an older, stronger, more experienced person is present, he will soon take over the leadership—either by pointing out the best place, or by taking someone's rucksack, or something similar; he might also draw the others' attention to some better way of jumping, thus trying to influence the course of the movement.

Now picture a teacher who does not just occasionally aid and advise someone younger than himself in a difficult situation but whose vocation is the long term work of making his pupils capable of meeting the tasks set by life.

The way to do this if the teacher had everything he needed, especially unlimited time and space, might be as follows: he would seek out as many such situations as possible with his pupils and allow them to experiment with them. These situations would have to be ones which can be found in man's natural environment. He would also give his pupils the opportunity to use tools and machines made by man—apparatus that required the use of feet as well as hands, such as ladders, wagons, steep stairs, etc., things that would give rise to a series of extremely valuable tasks. In this way the children would 'conquer the world' by moving in it, and in so doing they would not only be exercised physically but would also learn to judge a situation correctly and estimate rightly their own power to master it. They would learn caution and prudence and, since they are not alone in the world, consideration for others too.

All this, however fine, is scarcely possible in school. It is Pestalozzi's 'natural home gymnastics' (Pestalozzi, 1807) which still provide country children with some of their physical training but which are inaccessible to city children. At best the school can make use of them only occasionally on hikes and on camping expeditions.

For the main part of his work the teacher has to rely on the gymnasium and its apparatus, the courtyard, the playing field and the games apparatus to replace the opportunities of the natural environment for his pupils. To a certain extent this is true even of country school teachers, for even they cannot roam at will through forest and field with whole classes; they have to avoid ploughed land and meadows and nursery plantations. Empty land is becoming rarer and rarer in our over-cultivated European environment.

In this situation, the qualities 'unknown' and 'unexpected' are quickly lost. In the exercise places used year after year and week after week the variety of situations is simply exhausted and cannot be reproduced artificially. By restricting the work to the never-changing conditions of the exercise places at his disposal, the teacher may easily lose the perspective of the true needs for moving in the world outside. He may become entangled in traditional material. An important task for a theory of human movement is to liberate this perspective and thus create a serviceable basis for physical education.

The character of work in school forces one to adopt different methods from those of nature. One has to make do with the means provided; with their aid one has to create enough changing situations for whole classes to be able to practise the most important and characteristic functional activities essential for development, not without any danger at all—for danger is part of life and therefore of physical education too—but at least with the necessary regulations for safety.

This is true for all the branches of exercise. Swimming is an especially good example of how the school has to build up special teaching processes and how great the danger is of their getting out of touch with life. A swimming pool is really a very poor copy of rivers, lakes and the sea—but it makes it possible to teach whole classes without endangering the pupils' lives. It gives the pupils a foundation on which to build further; but swimming in the sea or in swiftly flowing rivers with all their difficulties and challenges has to be learnt afterwards separately.

The basis of all movement education is the purely purposeful form. For example, one barricades the gymnasium crosswise with apparatus and tells the pupils to get across somehow, either under or over or through it. Such tasks are relatively quickly exhausted and the teaching process then deviates from the natural process, for, although it would save effort if one were to slip through between the double bars, one tells the pupils to climb over them. The double bars symbolize a fence over which one climbs—this would be necessary in order to cross a real fence, although it is not actually necessary with the double bars. Ropes and laths too are not real obstacles but only 'mock-ups' of them. The situation is not reproduced as it appears in objective reality—a few features suffice. Certain general qualities of the apparatus, such as its firmness, erectness, the handholds and footholds it offers, make it a suitable representation of reality but compared with real situations these symbolic ones are poorer in every way.

In addition the life context is missing. Somebody jumping over a stream continues his walk on the other side or lies down to rest; in the gymnasium the activity stands alone having no connection with what goes before or after it. The real situation demands: 'get over this so that you can reach your goal'; the teacher demands: 'climb over these two bars'. The real situation demands: 'come down this meadow, the path runs down there by the corner of the forest'; the teacher demands: 'come down here in my ski tracks, pass between these two sticks'. These directions affect only where to go; they do not directly change the course of the movement. With a real stream one has to find out the easiest place to cross it; if one draws a 'stream' with two lines it can be jumped over anywhere, the only thing that matters is the relation of jumping ability to the width of the 'stream', and the latter is determined by the teacher, it is not given by nature; nor does one have to consider whether it might be better to wade through it or to build a path to help one across it. From the beginning it is a question of: jump over this 'stream'.

However, with this use of symbolic situations one has not left the field of purposeful movement even if the tasks are not quite the same as those set by nature. There would be little point in introducing the term movement task here; if one did, almost all the exercises used in the process of teaching would be movement tasks.

How can we make some progress towards a definition of the movement task? To compare once more the artificial setting of the gymnasium with the living context of functional activities: in the gymnasium the individual functional activities are practised for their own sake, unconnected with the past or the future and without reference to the reality of surroundings and other people who are present. For example, a group who are out hiking would need to stay together and to proceed with mutual aid and understanding, in the gymnasium this is quite unnecessary. Even if one is hiking alone one seldom merely walks. Here the view opens on to a valley or a mountain, now a bird calls which one would like to see, there a plant beckons one to look at it more closely—each time other movements enter the walking, intertwine with it, separate out of it by degrees until it again emerges in its pure form for a time. However, if in the gymnastic lesson the teacher were to ask the pupils just to walk round and round the room they would find it quite senseless for there would be nothing but the walking and they would rather play catch, where their running at least has a point.

One can observe that, to put it mildly, the activity does no good if all one's attention is upon it. Heinrich Kleist (1810) knew 'what havoc consciousness wreaks in human movements'.

Once aware of this one can make some noteworthy observations. For instance, a pupil, who was not very sure of herself in the water but just did separate stroke after separate stroke, had great difficulty in putting the length of the bath behind her. She was told to look up and smile after every stroke—and when on one of the last strokes she began to laugh it was clear that the battle was won.

Nevertheless, it is not just drawing away attention from it that 'helps' the activity. If it is combined with another activity the sequence gives rise to delicate transitions, the combination creates small changes in the course of the movement; many possibilities beckon, new paths seem suddenly to open up and the construction of the movement becomes much richer than when executed in stereotyped monotony. The movement needs these little deviations to become full and round; it is true that it has a clearly defined form, but this form is not rigid.

Despite the relative uniformity of the exercise places and despite the separation from a living context one can achieve sufficient variety when practising the activities if one sets the tasks in a certain way. This is not the only means of doing it, but it is a very useful means.

Of course one cannot combine every activity with every other activity. The various ways of progressing, for example, mutually exclude each other but when walking, running, jumping, one can look round, one can clap, wave, touch or seize something, one can throw or catch light objects, one can duck or bend down etc. This 'doing something else' distracts attention from the activity and the course of the movement is changed without one having expressly asked for a change. By looking round, neck reflexes come into play; the apparatus responsible for preserving equilibrium has to compensate for the turn—the pupil does not know it but in fact the co-ordination has taken place somewhat differently than it would have without the turn. The actual situation did not require the pupil to look round; the teacher added this determining factor but the pupil enjoys doing something a little more difficult so he is happy to go along with this unnecessary requirement. Children do such things by themselves too, without a teacher; one only needs to watch them playing hopscotch to see what unnecessary complications they impose upon themselves.

Such additional requirements are possible where the situation is not given in its complete, objective reality, with the result that the movement executed is not strictly and unambiguously related to the situation in all its details. It could, for example, occur in some real life situation that one has to lie down without one's feet moving from the spot, or moving only very little. Although there is no necessity for this when practising in the gymnasium the pupils can be asked to do it because . . . well, really only because one has observed that keeping the feet still like this varies the act of lying down in a certain way and this is what is wanted. There is no need to worry about whether or not there is an actual situation in which the additional demands are necessary; such exercises can be invented. However, one must not make the mistake of thinking that 'unmotivated variation' alone exhausts the possibilities of the movement task for teaching. The teacher setting movement tasks is extremely conscious of their purpose, which is to improve the form of a movement.

In conclusion it can be said that the movement task is a question of a functional activity which is changed and enriched by being combined with another functional activity or by additional requirements not determined by the situation. As far as method is concerned, the movement task is among the means of achieving good form in movement; whether it can also be used in other ways will be left open here. The movement task distracts the pupil's attention from the course of the movement and improves it in an indirect way.

5 Development and training of natural movement

Try measuring your greatness in knowledge
against your smallness in practical ability.
Nietzsche

So far an attempt has been made to show what natural movement is, but now the aim must be to point out one or two ways in which the teacher can help its development and training. Knowing and being able to impart knowledge, being able to do something and being able to teach it, are quite different things which often exist apart from one another.

How can the teacher fulfil his task of developing and training natural movement? What means is there of retaining natural movement; of regaining it when it has been lost; of making it a conscious, highly valued possession?

The answer to this question can be found by studying the development of children. When children first come to school they are usually capable of moving naturally without knowing anything about it. Their movements are skilful and therefore beautiful without being based on conscious exploitation of their physical capabilities. It is a pleasure to watch children of this age moving, and it is very characteristic that the children are not disturbed by being watched.

Of course there are sad exceptions, children who for inner reasons (temperament, illness) or for outer ones (the too bad or too 'good' living conditions of their parents) have prematurely lost their naturalness. In the busy bustle of our schools they cannot be treated individually, they go along with the others. Often just this not being specially noticed has an excellent effect.

This state lasts, on an average, up to the tenth or eleventh year. At about this time the freedom and beauty of movement of most children is lost and awkwardness and ungainliness take their place as the characteristic features of this age-group. Whilst children are not disturbed by being watched, adolescents are usually embarassed by even a hint of observation, or indeed the very thought of it. They are now conscious of their movements, and the sureness of the child, which was based on something quite different from consciousness, crumbles. From pure embarrassment boys and girls often adopt the silliest mannerisms of movement for a time.

Everyone knows that the hobbledehoy stage passes even when one does nothing about it. Precision, sureness, and beauty of movement return but they are of a different kind from that of a child. How far the individual consciously makes use of his body depends to some extent on whether his profession or some other occupation, a hobby perhaps, impels him to. It is probable that more people work 'consciously' than is generally accepted; at least the well-known 'working for profit' intimates that all those who do physical labour are familiar with the conception. It would be possible to link this joy in extracting an advantage from work with the carrying through of an education in correct working and everyday habits.

This whole development is always the same in broad outline, even when no intentional influence is exerted on it; indeed it is actually stronger than such an influence.

If one conceives education in general, and thus physical education too, as an aid to development and not as drill, naturalness of movement can only be retained by following the lines of development laid down by nature.

So between the ages of five and ten or eleven everything which might destroy naturalness of movement must be avoided. This is best done by setting the children problems of movement suited to their strength and allowing them gradually to find the best solution by themselves, by means of trial and error. Self-conscious training can only begin once the children have, by themselves, become aware of their movements but then it must be carried out in all earnestness; it has to be completed by the end of puberty. In adults one has to protect natural movement against habits or fashionable crazes injurious to health. To do this one can and must be able to count on the mental co-operation of the person exercising, which is quite different from the manner of working with children.

Since it is not only possible to destroy natural movement by deliberately drilling pupils in an unnatural style but also by making untimely demands on them, the whole of school physical education must be built up biologically. It is a prerequisite for teaching natural movement that the exercises, which are the

means of forming the body, be apportioned according to the
child's development and not, as so often, on the basis of some
artificial system. If for example, a physical education programme
demands that children between the ages of five and ten or eleven
learn gymnastic tricks on apparatus, even a good teacher, following the programme, can scarcely prevent their naturalness of
movement being destroyed.

School physical education programmes must be built up on a
biological basis, and every teacher should know the total programme not just that for the age-group he is teaching at the
moment. Only the teacher who knows the whole course of
development can give his work meaning by fitting it into the
greater whole. Without this knowledge it is easy to let the work
degenerate into the anxious observation of individual rules which,
overvalued at first, eventually disappoint. Work becomes trifling.

(a) *In the primary school*
In discussing the three main sections of development it is easiest
to give help and guidance for daily work by making the starting-
point the way of setting problems and the correction of faults. In
reflecting on what achievements can be expected from children
it must not be forgotten that there is no such thing as 'absolute'
achievement, and that every age-group has its own measure and
manner of achievement. And it is an established fact that achievements are completely reached at a later stage only if earlier
stages have not been omitted. Achievements are comparable with
fruits which take their time ripening.

A child living a happy life, free from external pressures, finds
many opportunities in his surroundings for achieving something.
A healthy child can to a certain extent pick and choose and he
tries himself out on problems to which his powers are equal and
which he can thus fulfil, but which carry a certain measure of
difficulty with them.

He tries, leaves it, tries again, until one fine day the ripe fruit
of attainment falls into his lap. The child is not aiming at this
result, he achieves it, so to speak, incidentally. Nature's patience
is still alive in him, whereas an adult, usually impatiently, tries
to attain achievement as soon as possible because he feels it to
be the most important thing.

Whilst a child with space, time, and opportunity chooses for himself, out of the many available, the movements he will attempt, the child in a gymnasium has the choice made for him. The child at school cannot choose for himself what he will do, for we rightly expect all the children to accept the problem they are set and to try to solve it. The teacher should, therefore, give very careful thought to his choice of exercises.

Fewest mistakes are made if the movements of daily life and work are kept in the foreground. The activities for this age-group, based on sound biological foundations, are running and jumping, pulling and pushing, lifting, carrying and throwing, mounting and climbing, while gymnastic tricks on apparatus should play only a minor part.

The amount of physical effort needed for these exercises is relatively large but the amount of conscious mental effort is small because the child does not consider in advance how he will perform the exercises; he tries all sorts of ways and gradually discovers the best solution for himself.

This way of working is based on the child's manner of development and must not be regarded as being of inferior value. It is the only thing to ensure the retention of naturalness of movement. So one should tell the children what to do and allow them to work out how they will do it completely by themselves.

How much they actually achieve in this way is of no importance at all for the time being. If the teacher himself overvalues achievement, and teaches his pupils at this stage to think it important, he will sooner or later destroy the form of their movement. For then joy is no longer the stimulus but rather ambition. As soon as the children think that they can get rewards or admiration for doing something, their movements become unnatural. In higher age-groups this is no longer true; then the pupils must learn to draw out of themselves the achievements of which they are capable, but at this age the whole group practises together, borne up and united by the pleasure they take in movement, and the individual is not singled out by his skill. Nor is there any final form of an exercise, which alone makes the comparison of achievements possible because all the children have to attain it.

Delaying measurable, so-called 'external' achievement does not mean that the exercises must all be easy, or more precisely, less profitable. The children themselves seek more difficult tasks as soon as they can do the easier ones, so the teacher too must set harder problems as the strength and capabilities of the children grow.

In all these matters only very exact, sympathetic observation of the life led by the children when no adult is near to supervise them is of any use; one has to get rid of one's inherited and habitual ideas and judgements—which are often not recognized as prejudices—and get to the point where one can truthfully say: 'the children themselves know much better than I do how they should go about that'. This is the surest way to be firmly in command and yet allow the children enough freedom for their naturalness of movement to develop and become refined.

In the faithful observation of games which develop outside school lies protection against a very common fault, which is the cause of much unnatural movement: a certain childish way of doing gymnastics. Women teachers in particular must be on their guard against this; whilst schoolmasters often try to force adult gymnastics on children ridiculously early, schoolmistresses sometimes never make the transition between the infant and the serious school child. For the first year at school, and even longer in some classes, much in children's gymnastics is reminiscent of playing with their own bodies, trying out their limbs; but soon school life with its seriousness and order brings about a practical adjustment; retaining the tone of voice used for children then has a merely childish effect and may hold up the development of large, unimpeded movements. So the teacher must try to develop a fine feeling for the tone of voice appropriate for five- six- seven- and eight-year-old children.

The question of representational exercises follows closely on this. It is well known that children can enter so strongly into a game that they forget reality. This can be exploited in gymnastics, and exercises, which for some reason have to be done, can be represented as work movements; the children are asked to show how this or that work is done. In this, as always, they move naturally; their imaginations put them in the place of the worker and the movement flows, one might say, from within them, and is not determined by the intellect but by an image. As long as the representation is fun for the children, it is a good means of attaining natural movement; instead of prescribing the movement in detail the teacher allows the children to represent the work, the animal, or the event, following their imagination. When the children no longer go along with this, one must stop, for tired, joyless representation has no value. The reason why a class does not go along with this sometimes lies in the teacher, he personally cannot work with this method and he just has to let it go at that; but usually the reason is that the children are growing up. At the age of nine or ten their whole attention is directed to the outside world; they want to grasp real objects, to work with real apparatus that they can hold; only in doing this do they learn.

Exercises with apparatus are an absolute necessity after a certain age, but the word 'apparatus' must be given a very wide interpretation and should include play apparatus as well as the familiar gymnastic apparatus. In addition it should be remembered that resistance does not come only from inanimate objects but also from class-mates; even a school with no apparatus can satisfy the need to grasp something and provide the experience of resistance. Where a school does possess apparatus the teacher may make use of it without having to fear a disruption of naturalness of movement. Of course, exercises with apparatus must not be chosen from a gymnastic point of view but according to our knowledge of the growth and development of children, they must be set problems and allowed to solve them as they will.

This needed to be said in so many words, since often the rejection of gymnastic tricks on apparatus for this age-group is taken as meaning the rejection of all exercises on apparatus. When properly chosen and executed, exercises on apparatus can do good service in developing natural movement.

It is necessary to mention here that developing natural movement cannot be entirely carried through by using only movements with a purpose. Expressive movements, where form is not determined 'by the purpose of the movements, but by the state of mind of the person doing them' (Klages, 1921), are a part of a complete education.

This aspect of physical education needs a sensitive and imaginative teacher who has a thorough understanding of movement. It is not easy to create an inner state, and merely making gestures is just theatre and only intended for spectators. When the lack of knowledge and understanding of movement, which still burdens many teachers, has given way to true education about it, physical education will be able to give dance the attention due to it. Meanwhile it is better to leave this part of physical education to the free games of the children, just seeing that they have enough space and time for their round dances and singing games.

The exercises, which can preserve and develop the naturalness of the children's movement, need to have names which the children will understand. There is no justification for gymnastic language as such at this stage; on the contrary, the more simply and ordinarily the children are asked to do something the more naturally they will carry it out. When one says to the first form 'turn to me' they certainly do it more naturally than if one commands 'left turn'; or 'all stand side by side' instead of 'form up in a line across the room'. All these expressions are abbreviations which can be taken into use as the children learn to understand them; but drilling these expressions into the children so that something seems to have been achieved when all goes off without a hitch, is a sure means of destroying naturalness of movement. Adults, accustomed to gymnastic terms, usually have to learn anew how to speak to the children when they come to teach the physical education lessons.

At first sight this may seem to be saying that instructions given in a language proper to gymnastics are capable of destroying natural movement but, considering for a moment how a voluntary movement is produced, one can see what importance is attached to the spoken expression used. When we wish to do something, an image of the action brings about the contraction of our muscles which we ourselves really know nothing about; it is, to be precise, wrong to say that we consciously innervate our muscles.

When one instructs a child, who knows nothing either of the language used in gymnastics or of his body, to do a movement either in anatomical or gymnastic terms, he receives no image of what he must do, and it is impossible for him to move freely and skilfully.

For similar reasons showing the children how to do the exercises is to be avoided at this stage. It puts a certain image of the movement before the child's eyes and he will then, if he is an obedient child, try to copy it faithfully, perhaps with no inner sympathy for the movement; in addition the search for the best form of solution by each individual is ruled out. Avoiding a demonstration does not mean that the teacher may not do the movement with the children. He can just say, 'Now we will do this or that' and he is naturally a part of that 'we'.

Pictures, which may be used in the class-room, must be chosen to correspond to the principle of natural movement. Pictures of how to do exercises are as much to be avoided as pictures of faults. Best are photographs of fine sculptures, pictures and photographs of animals and of children playing (bowling hoops, playing with balls, skipping, etc.). Their purpose is to teach the children to see the variety of movement in life, not to develop and fix in them the usual ideas of gymnastics and the demands they make for stylization.

For teaching at this level the teacher needs no special physical skill, only general physical agility. The movement problems solved by children will be able to be solved by adults as long as they have not completely neglected themselves physically, and those who have should not be teachers. For those who have no pleasure in movement and do not suffer if they lack it, will not easily be able to understand children, for whom movement is a necessity.

Naturalness of movement is destroyed especially easily and commonly by wrong correction of faults. One reproves something as a fault from an incorrect standpoint and, by so doing, takes away the child's artlessness. Many things which adults describe as faults are a matter of the child's not yet having learnt to do something, and correction is completely out of the question; the faults will disappear by themselves in time. Lack of style is no fault either, a child just has childish movements. Since children often change in their movements one has to be careful with the statement 'that is a fault'; it sometimes happens that a movement is done differently on the very next day. Only after longer observation can one say: this child has the incorrect habit of doing this in this way. Where there are habitual faults one must correct them; the child must become conscious that they are 'incorrect', but the word 'incorrect' must not be used for lack of skill. Real faults in the sense described are for example: the habit of breathing through the mouth, standing with the legs straddled or the feet turned outwards, pushing the hips forward, or holding the arms stiffly. Too much correction easily disrupts natural movement and makes the children self-conscious and unsure. One should first wait and see whether a certain fault will not disappear by itself, or whether one cannot correct it by distracting the child, by a joke which provokes laughter, by quicker timing, or by an interruption. Since pleasure stimulates movement (Klages, 1921) and probably enriches it too, one of the best ways of correcting faults in this age-group is somehow to make the practising pleasant; much succeeds in a moment of loud rejoicing which schoolmasterly seriousness could never have brought about. So too one must not suppress the natural shouting, laughing and talking which are the unavoidable result of some exercises, for example, wrestling, pushing and pulling contests; this would have a very bad effect on the freshness and naturalness of movement. It must just be kept within limits so that it does not degenerate into unruly noise. There is a certain kind of squeaking and squealing, especially in children from large towns, which actually increases spasmodically instead of subsiding when it is released, and this cannot be proceeded against too strongly.

Very many faults committed by children in gymnastics are merely the consequences of faults committed by the teacher, so one must always look for the faults in oneself first. Of course, they will not always be found in oneself, naturally they sometimes lie in the children. To correct real faults in movement one should make use of images; the reason for this lies in the way, described above, in which voluntary movements are brought about. The image of the scales and the sounding-lead can help even children to grasp the 'levelling out' into a position of equilibrium. Mentioning experiences of daily life provides many opportunities too. For example, when children are told to stand still at a signal there are always a few children who fall forwards after stopping because they have not regained their balance after the last step. If they are encouraged to watch carefully the way a car or a bus stops, it is then easy to make it clear to them how the vehicle sinks back into the position of rest, and the application to their own movements follows by itself. The delicate movement which can, for example, be seen in an Indian club or skittle just after it has been stood up, can help to awaken the picture of a position of rest which is not rigid and cannot be reached in one movement. Someone who has once grasped the essentials of natural movement will find a thousand opportunities in life for making them clear to children without falling into long-winded explanations. One cannot be referred often and persistently enough to the observation of animals as a means of learning; only from them can our eyes, blinded by the distractions of the city, learn to discriminate between beautiful and ugly movement and regain their simplicity of view. Even when dealing with children, people are often so influenced by ideas of style, fashion and propriety in movement that they find it impossible to learn to see things as they are; this faculty of true observation can only be practised on children when it has been acquired by the teacher.

To summarize: to train and develop natural movement in children up to the age of ten or eleven the teacher sets them suitable problems and leaves them free to solve them as they will. The period (necessary in the course of their development) of searching for and finding the solution best for each individual, must not be shortened by demanding deliberate work too soon. Play is the child's method of work. Correction of faults must be kept to a minimum and carried out in a manner suited as much as possible to children.

(b) *In the secondary school*

The second stage, puberty, is a transitional period. The good movement of the child is no longer there, that of the adult not yet present. Like all periods of transition this too, seen from outside, is unfruitful; the fruits of work done now ripen only later; in spite of all one's efforts pupils at this stage will seldom have completely good and natural movement.

For the pupils themselves this transition is not easy, for at first they are only conscious of the disruption of what they have hitherto possessed. They cannot yet know or understand that the old is giving way in order to make place for the new—the conscious mastery of their powers. The teacher needs much knowledge and sympathy to help his pupils over this phase. From the teacher's belief and confidence in the future they have to learn patience, and feel that they cannot go back or stand still now but must go forward; not to accept the difficulties of fighting through would be to cut off their own development.

For the teacher leading them, this is a very much more difficult and responsible time than when they were children. Naturalness of movement was then so strongly anchored in the child's
pleasure in movement that the teacher had only to let it be and
not supervise it too much; then there was 'life that still seems
fluid, sure of its laws but not conscious of them' (Spranger, 1924).
Now the boy or girl feels uncomfortable, does not know what to
do with his limbs; the urgent sense of joy which let the child play
so tirelessly and made his movements so free and beautiful, has
diminished. Now the intellect must take control, control which
before lay as if in the hands of Nature herself. A clearer, more
purposeful leadership is expected and demanded of the teacher.

The first factor of decisive importance for this is that the
teacher should understand how to show his pupils that naturalness of movement is something of value, and thus make them
willing to work on it themselves. Often children learn an
unnatural style of movement not because they want to but
because there is something which makes the child decide to take
pains with himself, such as love for a respected teacher, ambition
for a good report, or on account of a gymnastic display. In a
similar way there needs to be something to make the adolescent
take pains to work on natural movement. It must be represented
to him as being of real worth by its promotion of the health of
the individual, or of a satisfactory working life, for its artistic
value, or for the attainment of higher physical achievement.
People are not all equally capable of being moved by all these
benefits; according to their personal disposition this or that
benefit will make a deeper impression on them. This means
that the teacher must have various points of attack for showing
his pupils the value of natural movement. He needs to be versa-
tile in his approach so as to satisfy the various mental attitudes of
his pupils. His own personality and the character of the school
will naturally mean that one special benefit is emphasized and it
will determine the basic mood in which the work takes place; it
is all the more necessary that light should fall occasionally on
other values of natural movement which might otherwise pass
unnoticed.

The second determining factor is that, besides the conscious
exercising which will be the main subject of the following discussion, enough movement, not consciously controlled, should be

permitted. It is an error, which might easily creep in, to think that conscious exercise alone can preserve naturalness of movement and lead it over the dangers of puberty; this is not possible without abundant working off of high spirits in the freedom of nature. The adolescent needs something on which he can work and try out what he has learnt and practised a little, in order to make it a possession over which he has complete control. He also needs games and rushing about to create the experience which can then be worked out intellectually in the exercises. Only out of varied experiences does the characteristic of natural movement crystallize. To get the pure essence practice is needed in various types of exercise.

Intimate contact with the freedom of nature wakens and strengthens much instinctive control and confidence which would otherwise atrophy and which is quite indispensable. We cannot subordinate everything, all the time, to conscious control. An important part of developing and training natural movement is that young people should exercise in the open air.

If the pupil's life holds much outdoor physical activity in the form of work or walking to school or free play in leisure time, the gymnastic lesson need not contain much tumbling about. Achievement exercises, formative and, if necessary, corrective exercises are included and discussed—these form the material of the gymnastic lesson, and the pupils are told to observe and supervise their own movements. The teacher should often inquire what observations they have made and what their experiences have been, and in this way lead them.

If the pupil's life holds little physical activity, the gymnastic lesson must also provide the necessary amount of tumbling about. Outdoor activities such as games, athletics, skiing, etc., are a necessity, especially for town dwellers, not only in the interests of good health but also for the preservation and refinement of natural movement.

As on the one hand, unrestrained working off of high spirits is irreplaceable, so on the other, achieving good theoretical knowledge and assured performance is just as necessary. Natural movement is all too easily lost when it is not fostered, the more so as our way of life is to a great extent unnatural; many dangers besiege and threaten that which is taken for granted in people close to nature.

Here we will mainly be discussing conscious work on natural movement, i.e. exercises. This represents one part of physical education but it is not the whole of it. Enough space and time for working off excess energy is required; no one will achieve naturalness of movement with exercises alone.

The presentation of work for this age-group will be divided up in accordance with the same principles as the work with primary school children; yet the way in which one sets problems and corrects faults is certainly very different in childhood from what it is in youth.

In childhood problems are set which can be solved in any way the children wish; the goal is not a final form to be achieved by all the children, only as skilful an execution as possible. Measurable achievement is not the goal to be aimed at. It makes no difference where the problems are set, whether in a playground, in a gymnasium, in the snow, or in water; it is always the searching and trying which gradually lead to a solution best for each individual and this characterizes the working method of children.

This method of working has a strong similarity with the way in which a very young child learns difficult movements like walking and talking: that is, without 'thinking'. He carries out the movements without working them out in advance, testing them out, groping for them by instinct alone. From his movements he learns and gathers experience which makes him more and more capable of moving as he expects and wishes.

An adult on the other hand is capable of imagining movements before he executes them. He shortens the path of learning by not having to go through all the possibilities but by trying them out in his imagination, so he 'hits' on the new movement after only a few tries, or perhaps even at the first try, and is ready for the main work, the filing away, the working at technique. It is scarcely necessary to say that here, as in the rest of nature, no sharply defined line separates the two phases. In a schoolchild the childlike method of trial and error alternates with the adult method of learning—using the imagination—although the extent to which the two intermingle depends on personal disposition and practice. In puberty too, the childlike method of working is not completely eliminated; indeed it never is completely eliminated, even an adult often continues to show such traits. This is not something to be regretted, for people who have kept much of this method of working remain young in their movements. They have a greater variety of movements, and subtlety of distinction between movements, than people who have settled for one possibility.

Good training in movement technique has to reckon on a gradual change-over and a continuation of the child's manner of learning; it cannot and must not try to achieve everything by conscious exercising. This is a second reason for the importance of allowing adolescents the opportunity to run about freely and vigorously as well as to perform set tasks. The more the child-like elements have been atrophied or destroyed by lack of movement or incorrect teaching, the more difficult is training in the period of puberty. It demands strong will-power and great stamina from the pupils if they are, with all the means of conscious exercising open to them, to regain that which a lucky person has managed to salvage from childhood—if they are able to succeed at all.

A certain insight into the different methods of learning in children and adults should be imparted to adolescents, but without going into too much detail. Then they understand much more easily the essentials in learning new movements.

The ability to practise a new movement until it has become part of one and proceeds as if by itself is usually called 'automatization', or instead of this word, one used by Klages (1921), 'vitalization'.

This vitalization is what the pupils must learn. It hides the secret of all skills learnt by exercising, and is the path from knowledge to ability. It is a life process never brought about by 'teaching' and 'learning'. It can happen even without one's being aware of it, as we often learn something without having the slightest idea how. However, we can let the light of consciousness fall on this life process and we gain something thereby: that is, the ability to intervene in it, which we did not have before. We can, to a certain extent, regulate it. We gain full, conscious mastery over our powers.

Since the usual movements like walking, running, lifting and carrying, pulling and pushing, are to a great extent already 'vitalized' by this age, they do not offer much opportunity for coming to understand this process; we already know how to do them. The pupils too, are inclined to undervalue these common movements; they think they cannot learn anything from them because they are so familiar. Young people grasp eagerly at unusual or exciting movements; understanding of the intellect-tual content of daily life only comes later. Nietzsche's fine words: 'Life is a handicraft which must be thoroughly, unremit-tingly learnt and practised unsparingly, if it is not to allow botchers and chatterers to creep out' can only be grasped in their true meaning by those of riper years. So now, especially in gymnastics, art forms (see glossary) come into their own, and with them a special language with simple descriptive terms. Nobody would try to replace expressions like vault, rear-vault, crouch-jump, upward circles, etc., by paraphrases out of daily language. In the age-group for which such exercises are right, the description of them naturally comes into use.

As long as a sound training in natural movement comes first, art forms are a good starting-point for training in movement technique. From the unaccustomed problems and new series of movements it is easier to see how learning proceeds than from familiar movements, which one can no longer imagine having had to learn with such effort. New things command attention. This is, by the way, why an adult can learn so much from, for example, a foot injury; the wish to avoid certain movements because they hurt brings a change in the habitual way of walking, and then one notices all sorts of things of which previously one was not aware.

In order to practise a new movement attention is given to individual points in its course; details are extracted and pulled into the light of consciousness, thus bringing them under control. One studies, for example, the way the tension changes when a movement is done, the rising and falling of power; or one watches its action in the confines of the body, how it swings through the joints. No attention is paid to the effect of the movement on the external world but only to the movement itself.

When a new movement has been thought out and grasped intellectually from various points of view it is repeated and, whilst great care is taken to retain all that has been learnt, it is 'practised'. This continues until its course does not vary even when no special attention is paid to it, until the movement as a whole is mastered. Then greater strength, or increased speed is added to it, as the purpose of the movement demands: that is, one attends to the effect of the movement on the external world and tries to regulate it accordingly. The highest degree of perfection is reached when the movement achieves its purpose with the greatest efficiency.

It is clear that such exercising demands continual intellectual attention, resulting from constant observation of the movement. Learning does not take place unless full attention is given to the work, and at the worst this may even din in some fault. This type of exercising requires concentration, otherwise it would be better to play and run about as the time spent doing this is not lost. It therefore follows that pupils in this middle stage should not have all their gymnastic lessons late in the day because the work demands intellectual freshness.

The degree of physical strain is not directly connected with the degree of intellectual strain. One can graduate the intellectual and physical tension in a gymnastic lesson independently of each other. This gives the teacher an opportunity for attuning the lesson in every respect to the strength of his pupils.

The skill that has been won is tried out and worked through in various ways and with increasing intensity, until it is fluent. The clumsiness of the beginner is lost, and gradually, to a greater or lesser extent, mastery is achieved.

This quite different method of working determines the way of setting problems and is very dissimilar to that used in childhood. It is no longer sufficient to present the pupils with movement problems which they can solve in any way they wish. Now, from the many possible, the pupils must find the best solution—they must develop a good technique. The individual can work for himself; the problem is personal to him, for all good technique is personal. The individual has liberty within a general conformity with the laws of nature.

From here a short, straight path leads to the recognition of natural movement. To recognize and feel this is the goal to which the pupils must be led, through many intermediate steps, and at each step they must be conscious that it is leading them to the goal. The teacher must try 'to attach to the pupils a chain of attainable tasks arising from that ideal', that is, he must show them in detail what impedes natural movement and what furthers it.

Details are practised on their own and when performed fluently are reinserted into the general course of the movement. So, for example, the pupils practise letting the relaxed limbs fall down separately, thus becoming conscious of the effect of gravity on each part of the body. However, these movements do not occur as exercises important in their own right but as a means of approaching natural movement, otherwise the hierarchy of values is destroyed in the pupil.

Each technique that has been learnt must be re-worked into the movement from which it has been taken; the pupils must not just be able to do something for its own sake, but must learn to apply it. This is recognized as their skill and is measured by what can be seen to be attained by it, that is, by their achievement. The degree of achievement is the measure of their mastery over their powers. Achievement is not a goal to be reached, but a measuring-rod of skill.

It takes stamina and perseverance to gain skill. The pupils do not practise now as children practise, clutching now at this, now at that; but all their forces are gathered to a point to achieve what they set out to do. The goal must be kept firmly in view, and they must learn to bear the tension which accompanies all striving. This is a fruitful opportunity for developing will-power.

The general psychological character of this age-group alone would forbid one to go on working with them as if they were children. To take a characteristic example: jumping is an exercise beloved by pupils of all ages. Children hop about out of the pure joy of living, they do not want to achieve anything by so doing, or to show or prove anything to themselves or others; the movement seems to flow from the turmoil inside them, it is purposeless, a game. The adolescent boy or girl stands opposite an obstacle with tense attention and collected powers before jumping over it, proud of his or her own strength and skill. The movement is willed and consciously controlled to a much greater extent; considerable practice takes place before this voluntary movement is produced by the body like one proper to it, flowing from inside it. The child lives happy and untroubled in the present, the adolescent reaches into the future. Thus nothing seems more unbearable to him than standing still, at least to the more intelligent adolescent. So, in the problems which are set to pupils of this age-group there must be much higher tension than in those for children, who only wish to make movements in general, whereas the adolescent wishes to achieve something. All the faculties which now develop must be utilized and be forced to co-operate. Problems must be set in such a way that they cannot be solved without this co-operation: stronger concentration, greater stamina, heightened observation, the power of comparing and judging. Even the often unlovable intractability and familiar egotism of this age-group can be exploited: the pupil exercises in every sense for himself—he himself will progress by exercising, will improve his movements and win a good personal technique. Just as team games are necessary at this age for the preservation of good health and for education, so, on the other hand, individual exercises are necessary, like those in gymnastics, swimming and athletics, in which the individual can work on his own and has no need of others for the exercise itself. Here there appears to be an inner psychological need to have these different forms of physical activities going on together.

In training and developing natural movement with this age-group problems must be set which demand more difficult, more intellectual work, and the solution of them should be the one which can be recognized as the natural one, which corresponds to the body's laws of movement and allows the highest achievement. The demand that all the powers of the mind should be involved must be strongly indicated by the way in which the problems are set. Suitable problems for the various fields can be collected into a plan if one has abundant experience but this plan must not be conceived as something rigid and unchanging. The ability to solve certain problems is not a goal which must be reached by the class but a standard for measuring how far the members of the class have come in mastering their bodies. The tension in their work which is absolutely necessary at this age (and the teacher must hold the reins especially firmly, but at the same time delicately) must be felt by the young people as a deep respect for what is best in them. In the final resort, this is a question of the teacher's personality and words are not of much avail here. A living current of give and take, which goes far beyond the merely physical, passes between teacher and pupils. Education is not to be realized in any other way.

It is of no consequence which branch of physical exercise one starts from in order to clarify the essence of natural movement and build up a method of training movement technique. One can just as well begin with swimming as with gymnastics, athletics or skiing. According to factors of place and space, one branch or another will be chosen as a starting-point, preferably the one which, in the circumstances of the school, will provide the richest opportunities but the pupils also need to make progress in a second field, one as different as possible from the first. So, for example, swimming with its gliding advance, without firm support, would be, from the point of view of movement technique, an excellent counterpart to gymnastic apparatus work with its special peculiarities of movement. If the pupils work exclusively in one field limitation is hard to avoid; they think that the principles refer only to this and not to other fields. It is essential for the comprehension of natural movement to recognize it as valid everywhere. Physical education has the particular duty of giving a unified training in movement technique, and of making the pupils aware of it.

With the conditions prevailing in our schools and in our climate, gymnastics will very often be one of the fields. This will be so for years to come, and may well always be so in the larger towns.

Using gymnastics for work on natural movement has its advantages and disadvantages; the enclosed space narrow sattention and thrusts a person into himself; this encourages thoughtful exercising. However, it is essential to include at least one activity in the open air, for in gymnastics there are two possible dangers. In the first place, the idea of disciplined 'strengthening' gymnastics has been strongly held, and this makes the temptation to work with a large expenditure of energy very great. Whereas in long drawn-out activities, which usually take place out of doors, one must husband one's energies and keep a reserve back for unforeseen events; conserving energy becomes a matter of course.

In the second place and as a reaction to this excessive expenditure of energy there may be a striving for looseness. Looseness of movement maybe regarded as a goal, and loosening exercises as the be-all and end-all of exercises for physical good form, whilst they are in fact only a medicine or a means for making the pupils aware of the degree of tension. In exercises like swimming, skiing and skating, in which the essential is to keep one's balance, both stiff and loose movements are soon revealed as impossible, and natural movement, hovering in equilibrium, as correct.

There is yet another reason why gymnastics on their own are unfavourable. For in gymnastics one soon reaches the limit of intensification; one is in command of the simple movements and has to find new difficulties if one is not to stand still. Then there is a danger of falling into artificiality, and, without realizing it, working according to the universally accepted picture of a 'good gymnast', and having a one-sided conception of achievement. This greatly endangers natural movement.

In hiking, swimming, skiing on the other hand, the changing terrain, wind, weather, current, type of snow, are always creating new difficulties. How often a person believes himself to be competent at an activity, and is suddenly faced with new problems. The ability to perform these activities is never really perfect, it can always be improved by practice.

The basic method for the correction of faults has already been given in the earlier discussion. This is essentially a matter of replacing an incorrect movement, which has become habitual, by a newer, better one. Therefore, what has already been said about learning new movements is also valid for correction.

In this age-group too one must not try to correct everything with conscious exercising. Many things improve by themselves when the teaching in general is good. Much can still be effectively influenced by the means used mainly with children such as distraction, visual images, etc., but, whilst conscious exercising could be demanded of children only to a very modest extent, in the transitional phase between childhood and adulthood it forms the most important and characteristic means of correcting faults, and must as such be carefully developed.

Bad habits retained from childhood must now be condemned much more strictly than before, and the teacher must demand that the pupils make serious efforts to get rid of them. Friendly, patient reminders are no longer in place, one cannot work for ever on the same trivialities or one never gets any further. A clear explanation, concise but adequate, of why this habit is harmful and how it can be corrected is given, and then it is not discussed further except perhaps by a short reminder to someone who continues with the fault; the teacher should try to strengthen the general desire for progress rather than being too busy with individuals. Strong class spirit has greater influence than continual reminders from the teacher.

The battle against bad habits (breathing through the mouth, standing and walking with the feet turned out, standing with crossed arms or the hips pushed forward, etc.) must not take up much time in the lesson, otherwise too little time will remain for the real work which should be done by this age-group.

Since conscious improvement of movement demands mental freshness one cannot yoke the pupils to this work every time one wants to. When pupils are mentally fatigued some faults must be allowed to pass, especially those which result from inattention; when something has not yet become part of the pupils but is in the process of being learnt, the old fault easily creeps in again when attention falters. At such a time the teacher can only remind them, with a short admonition, of something which has already been explained and which they understand. There would be little sense in explaining something new, this must be left for a more suitable moment.

Nor would it be right for the teacher to correct a fault immediately it is noticed. There is an occasion when every fault is especially well-defined, and when its disadvantages become obvious; this is the right time to open battle against it. This moment often occurs when the pupils are striving to do something and cannot because they always make a certain mistake in their movement. Success in correcting faults depends to a large extent on knowing how to seize the right moment.

It is scarcely necessary to say that there are grave and slight faults and that the grave ones must be conquered first. The slight ones can be discussed too, but by the tone of correction the pupils should be able to feel a difference between them and the grave faults. The fewer big faults there are in a section of the work the more time can be given to correcting the small ones. However, if the teacher points out all the faults at once to a class still wrestling with difficulties, the pupils become frightened and despairing; with all the good will in the world they have not enough powers of concentration to attend to more than one matter at a time.

The teacher must also avoid combating faults by means of negatives. By saying 'this is not correct' an impediment is implanted in the pupil which prevents him from doing what he has done up to now, but does not tell him what to do instead. So as soon as the pupils' attention is drawn to a fault, or, in other words, it is brought to consciousness, it must be carried to its conclusion and the pupils must be able to see clearly the goal towards which they are working. It is therefore a principle that the teacher says to the pupils: 'You must not do it this way, but like this.'

This is, of course, not always easy, but it is better for the pupils not to know that they have a fault, than for them to know it and become unnatural and embarrassed without being able to work at improving it. If the teacher himself is not really clear where the fault lies it is better for him to say nothing for the time being. Only very conscientious observation and comparison gradually develop the ability not only to recognize faults as such, but also to see at first glance where the point at which one should begin correcting it lies.

This insight can be gained by the teacher in lessons given to individuals or small groups much more quickly than in the normal class lessons, in which the teacher usually has to teach many pupils at the same time and also attend to class organization and discipline. Such opportunities should be seized wherever they occur. Occasionally it also helps to watch individuals or a small group of pupils during a whole lesson, in all their movements, more carefully than is normally possible. In doing this more is seen than when the teacher's attention is divided among all of them. This presumes that the teacher has the members of the class firmly in control, and that their will to work seriously has already been secured.

The goal is that the teacher should be able to say exactly where the correction should take place: whether at the beginning of the movement or during it, whether muscles, which should be doing little work, are doing too much, whether there is too little tension, whether a joint is being held rigid instead of being taken up and carried forward by the movement, and so on. If the whole form of the movement is wrong the most helpful thing for the pupil is a comparison, watching the wrong and right forms side by side, or one after the other. If, for example, a knee-bend is being done incorrectly as far as the form of the movement is concerned, either the teacher demonstrates first an incorrect and then a correct knee-bend, or he has two pupils perform the movement at the same time, one showing the right and the other the wrong form. A very effective means of understanding movement form is by drawing. Pupils who, for some reason, are not taking part in the lesson should be encouraged to watch and to draw. After such a lesson many will have had a living experience of how one can learn from the mistakes made by others. Drawing is the best way of learning how to make exact observations and grasp forms, and much more use could and should be made of it in movement education.

The goal of natural movement is reached by 'a chain of attainable tasks' (Nietzsche). The next step to be taken towards the goal must be shown to the pupils, then the next, and so on, otherwise their confidence, so essential for further work, is easily lost. In this method of teaching all the help that is possible is given to the pupils. The teacher somehow simplifies each step to be taken and shows the pupils that this step leads towards the goal and that there is no reason to allow their courage and faith to sink, for it will be reached in the end.

Progress built up carefully step by step is the condition for effective correction of faults. When a teacher takes over a new class he should first limit himself to exact observation of which faults occur, which are committed by all the pupils and which by individuals only; he should try to win an insight into what their basis is, whether it is personal predisposition, living conditions, or past schooling. Only when he knows the pupils well can he build up the plan which will be the foundation of future work. Of course this plan must not be followed obstinately; changes are often necessary in the course of work even with the best thought-out plans, because the teacher can never know in advance how the means he intends to use will work, or how the pupils will react to them physically and mentally; but once he knows the pupils he can fix at least a guiding line for work. He can, as it were, sketch in the path along which he hopes to draw his pupils towards the goal of natural movement.

Two examples picked at random may serve to explain further what is meant by this.

Suppose that the teacher is taking over a new class which up to now has kept the arms stiff instead of using the joints of the arms in movements. It will not be of much use to tell the pupils not to keep their arms stiff. The first thing to do is to avoid exercises in which there is much danger of stiffness and encourage exercises that involve movements in the joints of the arms.

The pupils can play games with small balls. Throwing the ball up and catching it again; each pair of pupils throwing two balls at a time and counting a point if both balls are caught, playing with three or even four balls to each pair of pupils, such games with small balls demand precise arm work and will help to lessen stiffness in the arms.

Pulling and pushing exercises too—not contests—in which, among other things, attention is paid to correct arm work, are good.

Parallel to this runs the work one does with the ultimate aim of making the pupils understand the general principle of the interplay of the joints, and the teaching of the application of this principle. The teacher draws their attention to this on many and various occasions, when they are swimming, playing, or just making everyday movements. He tells the pupils to watch how children playing freely, and animals, use their joints, and then to watch their fellow-pupils and make comparisons.

Amusing exercises—such as pretending to be dead; carrying an 'unconscious' person; falling down noiselessly and without hurting oneself; hopping like a sausage with dangling limbs—help to reduce tension and teach the pupils how to let themselves go, without this ability becoming over-emphasized in their minds.

Then follow swinging exercises in which the 'flying' of the arms and their swinging to rest like a pendulum at the end of the movement is recognized; an amusing exercise for this is the 'top': one turns on one's own axis, slowly at first and then faster and faster, whilst the arms, like attached ribbons, follow the movement and fly round. If they were weightless this would not happen.

The next step is consciously letting the raised arms drop, and actually, if the expression can be used, it is a dropping divided into parts; the pupil must observe how

clearly each part of his arm has its own movement, and
how all the joints have a part to play.

Then he returns to the point of departure and sees that this is
so in the ball games and in pulling and pushing, etc. Not only in
the passive movement of letting the arm fall, when it is abandoned
solely to gravity and the muscles are inactive, but in work with
the arms as well, the parts of the arm must be fully used. There
is no sense in stiffening a joint by contracting the muscles where
the ability to work rests fundamentally on the movement in the
joints. Nature has certainly not divided the arm into sections so
that man may wilfully make it solid again. When they recognize
this, the pupils will understand all that is necessary, and they will
in part also be able to do it; what is still missing must be won
by each individual by means of persistent work on himself.

Another example: the pupils are walking badly; their
steps are not long or elastic enough; their way of walking
does not flow. The main fault and the one which must be
attacked first is the slow progress being made, for this
contradicts the meaning of walking. The teacher must
first awake in the pupils a feeling for the movement forwards. For this, running is better than walking, for the
striving to advance is expressed more strongly in it.
Especially long bounding runs should be practised often,
and running which starts off slowly and gets faster.

Once the pupils have begun to grasp the way their
bodies are thrust forward into space when they do this, it
can be worked on when they are walking with very large
steps, or walking very fast. At the same time a flowing
sequence of movement can be attained by walking and
running to music, or to a drum-beat, or to gentle clapping.

All kinds of running exercises in the form of games
(running in pairs and turning a full circle when told to, or
swinging each other round as one runs) help too to
awaken the feeling for smooth progression.

Then the teacher introduces special exercises such as
practice in exercising the elasticity of the legs and the
correct moment for lifting the leg; where necessary a few
localized exercises for individual joints (taken as a

functional unity) may be included, for example, rocking on the feet for the ankle-joint; walking with exaggeratedly high steps to make the hip-joint flexible.

Details such as how the feet are held, and the distribution of the weight of the body on the soles of the feet are explained and tried out in movement examples. In short, all the individual skills needed for good walking are explained and practised by means of partial movements suited to the purpose.

When most of the pupils understand and can do them they are once again built into the total movement the teacher is working to improve. For example, they practise the correct positioning of the feet, which is now familiar to them, whilst walking slowly—that is, the pupils are told to concentrate on this one aspect and to forget everything else for the time being. In this way the movement gradually improves.

The course of correction of faults described here is not followed through step by step purely as a sequence in time, but everything is woven in together. It is quite safe to interrupt something and take it up again some time later. Whole lessons must not be given to work on walking only: the lesson also serves other purposes. The only important thing is to keep all the threads in hand, however tangled they may become, and not to drop one. More plainly: the teacher joins battle against only a part of the fault present in the pupils, but once he has done so he perseveres energetically until the victory. The teacher's art is to decide which faults he intends to overlook. Faults are in some way all interdependent and, as work proceeds, many will disappear by themselves without special effort.

How many faults can be corrected by conscious exercising depends in part on the time available. During the professional training of physical education teachers as many faults as possible will be corrected but in school, only a few at a time. The general intellectual demands made on the pupils, the position of the physical education lessons in the school day (first or last lesson), and also the receptivity for this work which often differs greatly from class to class, all play a role in this. Occasional correction, such as is suitable for children, is never enough for this age-group;

young people must go through the process of refining a movement at least once.

Before concluding these considerations by giving the educational reasons for requiring the correction of faults to be carried
out in this way, it is desirable to mention the question of whether
the teacher of this age-group should show his pupils how to do
the exercises. For children this is rejected, at least in its usual
form, but with adolescents it is fully justified, if the teacher
makes use of it sensibly and in moderation. It often heightens the
pleasure of exercising, which at this time is beginning to slacken,
if the teacher demonstrates an exercise well; this can be a great
stimulus.

Demonstration, in the sense of showing what is correct and
what is not, has already been mentioned as being justified. It is
an indispensable means of teaching, for many details of movement training can be explained only by being shown. Words
often do not lead to the goal. Thus a teacher, who for some reason
cannot demonstrate the exercises, can work better with children
and adults than with adolescents. Careful, patient repetition of a
sequence to be learnt, overcoming a point at which one always
stumbles, working a detail already practised into the course of
a movement—these are all things which can more easily be
shown than put into words. The same is true for exercises with
a definite form of execution, and therefore for art forms (see
glossary) of every kind.

Demonstration serves thus, on the one hand, to show the final
form of the exercises which is to be achieved: an artistically correct vault, or a technically good long-jump from take-off, or a
correct dive into the water; on the other hand, it offers the
opportunity to show conscious practising and improvement of
one's own movement by example. Nothing is as stimulating and
convincing as when the teacher learns with his pupils something
he could not previously do.

In each individual case it must be clear to the pupils whether
the demonstration is meant as an explanation or as a challenge.
If the former, nobody expects them to copy it: they are just
supposed to learn something from it. If the latter, however, they
are being shown what they must achieve.

A teacher misuses demonstration worst of all if he uses it to
show off to his pupils, and have them marvel at his skill.

To conclude this section, a few words on the general educational value of well carried out correction of faults.

Before all else, this is an exercise in perseverance. There are not many faults which give way at a first assault; usually only persistent exercising leads to the goal. In doing this the pupil also learns skill in dealing with himself. If the demands of the self-imposed tasks are too great he will easily fall into hopeless self-depreciation and give up the battle, but if he proceeds by short steps he is more likely to reach the goal in the end. He learns to evaluate his own powers and capabilities, and with patience may find opportunities for extracting profit even from his own weaknesses. There is never any sort of success in the battle against faults without conscientious, honest work; every evasion of a difficult point, every cowardly avoidance, takes its revenge. This is true in other fields as well, but in the intellectual field the results of dishonest, careless work are more difficult to recognize, they are not as obvious as here, where everything is at once physically visible. Thus it is more easily comprehended here, and the point at which to begin improvement is more easily found. Education towards honest work and complete faithfulness in small matters in physical exercise may influence the pupil's work in other subjects. The pupil may take these values from the realm of physical work, in which they are more easily gained, and transfer them to the realm of intellectual work.

(c) With adults

Although, strictly speaking, a discussion of exercising with adults does not belong within the confines of this work, a few remarks on the subject will round off the discussion.

When attempting to answer the question of how adult gymnastics and natural movement stand in relation to one another, one must distinguish between three cases. First, the participants have enjoyed a good education and are at the stage they should have reached; they move in a natural manner and consciously work at moving even better. Then work with them is simply a continuation of what has already been done, more and more delicate filing-away, more and more conscious application to a wide variety of activities. One cannot quite give up conscious work even when the highest possible perfection has been attained, for professional work and life continually threaten what has been won. Without continual care natural movement will not easily survive for long under our living conditions.

Second, the people with whom one is to work have managed to salvage naturalness of movement out of childhood into maturity, either owing to a propitious way of life, or due to a specially strong predisposition. However, they are scarcely conscious of possessing a treasure and so they may forfeit it before they are aware of it. If chance alone has preserved naturalness, then a strong temptation to imitate a film star who moves affectedly, in a studied way, photographs in a magazine, a gymnastic demonstration unnaturally stylized, etc., can just as easily harm or destroy it. Such people can quickly attain an understanding of natural movement since they are already capable of it. They possess the ability, and it is just a case of becoming aware of what they have been doing without conscious purpose.

The third case is the most unfavourable: natural movement has been destroyed, whether by incorrect training, bad predisposition, or unpropitious circumstances. In a shortened and condensed form the whole development which the child goes through on its way to maturity must be repeated. So: begin with lots of easy, happy movement, which should be play in the sense in which Schiller (1794) used the word, and must also be felt as such; make a gradual transition to conscious practice of details which are explained in a simple, visual way; then work the knowledge gained in this way into the flow of the movement, thus refining it.

For these people, regaining naturalness of movement by learning to recognize it may be impossible, they may have too little of their original feeling for natural movement left for it to be revived and improved. However, even in seemingly bad cases a surprising amount of progress can be made, it just needs a great deal of confidence and patience on the part of the teacher. Anyone who thinks he can force a quick success here is on the wrong path from the beginning. This too, like the regular development of children, is a process which takes time, and can at the most only be hastened a little by human efforts. It often takes two or three years before the latent bodily awareness begins to stir and accepts the details worked out by the intellect so that they take root and grow. These then are the beginnings of developments in the dormant life of movement.

Section II

Education in good posture and movement

Posture education needs special discussion because it was for a long time carried out in a totally unbiological manner. So we will show in context how posture education in school can be carried out, being based on the structure and peculiarities of the upright position. This will also produce guiding lines for the shaping of exercises of the trunk.

By observing posture in a school one gains a sure idea of the kind of gymnastics practised there; free, natural posture of the children is, it is true, not its only goal, but it is a very important one. If a school doctor notices that the classes led by a certain teacher have especially good posture, this is indeed praise for the teacher concerned. And when one considers that although 'posture' has a physical basis which must be carefully kept in mind, it can never be achieved through the body alone; one realizes that no teacher who is not an educator can achieve anything in this field.

Good posture cannot be achieved by means of a few exercises scattered here and there in the gymnastic lesson. All exercise affects it. In children especially, posture is not yet something fixed, determined; growth is continually taking place and only by about the seventeenth year has personal posture become fixed. Only by making biologically correct demands on the body can every child, in the course of time, achieve his best. So the concept 'good posture' determines both the choice of exercises and the manner in which they are to be carried out; for there are exercises which harm posture and they must be inexorably eradicated from the syllabus. As well as this, one must make sure that clothing is not constrictive, that the 'sedentary school' disappears, that the time that has to be spent sitting at desks contains enough breaks for exercise, and, not least, that care is taken to foster good breathing.

All this belongs to posture education—one can see that this is a matter for the school, not just for the individual teacher. What use is it if the feet are placed parallel in the gymnastic lesson, and then on some special occasion, when the child has to recite a poem, the feet are fashionably turned out; or if the physical education and music teachers teach the children to breathe in different ways?

Even when one considers good posture as something purely physical, it is of great value to health and the school has a duty to equip its pupils with it for life. Good posture has the greatest importance for the undisturbed course of all the processes necessary to the smooth running of the body, such as circulation, breathing, digestion, etc., and is therefore a goal of physical education which must be taken very seriously.

The first and most important requirement for the development of good posture is that children should have plenty of physical activity. If children had the necessary space and time for rushing about, at least the healthy ones among them would tumble around sufficiently to be able to develop well physically, just like animals growing up in the wild, for this rich and varied movement would provide enough stimulus for their development.

In cities there is scarcely a child with enough space and time to satisfy his desire for movement; we have already forgotten how much a child needs, and usually think we have done a lot if we merely give him an hour's walk. From this it follows that one of the important tasks of physical education is to assure at least the minimum of physical movement necessary, but of course there is an indissoluble contradiction between this task and the time available. For over a hundred years doctors have been demanding a daily period of exercise, if, at the least, the harm done by schools themselves is to be repaired. And today we have at best four, and at worst two periods of exercise weekly in our schools. So one must never think that the physical education lessons in school can really give the children the necessary amount of movement; one must strive untiringly to bring the parents to see that their children get enough exercise, and to make it generally clear how much is needed beyond what is done by the school in physical education.

Even if the home always fulfilled its task of providing space and time for the child's urge for movement, physical education would not become superfluous because the school has a second important task, which the home cannot fulfil. The school must educate its pupils in good posture and movement. For this a

teacher is necessary. Working to improve his posture and movement for aesthetic and health reasons does not have the same
appeal for the child as working for high achievement. Training
for good form appeals to the ethical in man but training for high
achievement is what grips his interest and enthusiasm. A healthy
child finds the latter by himself in his desire for movement and
games; he needs the direction of a teacher to attain the former.

So one could also say that this task is more properly a part of
physical education than the first, which it has to fulfil nowadays
only because the home usually does not do so sufficiently. However, as we will show, training in form can only be provided in
and through work on achievement; one could not therefore
eliminate this from the physical activities in school even if the
home did give enough scope for movement. Perhaps the educational task of physical education can best be explained by a
comparison with reading: English lessons can never contain all
the children's reading but they must foster the pupils' reading
in order to teach them to read correctly, and to educate them in
understanding, discrimination and taste—they must give intellectual leadership in the world of literature. Physical education
has a similar task in the world of movement.

For the teacher a clear recognition of the basic structure of the body and the laws resulting from it is of fundamental importance. Posture education is impossible without this recognition, which is based on knowledge of the anatomy of the body. If one wishes to retain harmony between form and achievement one must aim at achievement based on the laws of the body, not antagonistic to them.

The exterior shape of the body depends, apart from certain parts which will be individually treated, on the adjustment of the skeleton, that is, on the position of the bones in relation to one another. So if one wishes to work on the form of thè body one must try to influence this adjustment. In all movements the bones move in relation to each other. The pupil must be brought to feel this in himself—first of all the great adjustments which occur in large, spacious movements, and eventually the smaller, delicate adjustments on which changes in posture depend.

For good form one also needs a certain development of the muscles; this has always been considered one of the goals of gymnastics and has therefore usually been achieved. However, it is a mistake to believe that posture training can be achieved solely by strengthening the muscles. As will be shown more fully later, posture correction is essentially a matter of changing the pull of the muscles.

(*a*) *The movement process*
In order to show the connection between the bones and the muscles, we will first include a general consideration of what happens when a movement takes place.

As soon as we want to move, our muscles contract, and they can do so to about one-half of their length. The two ends of a muscle are fastened to two different bones which are connected to one another in a mobile relationship by means of a joint.

When a muscle is contracted a movement takes place in the joint spanned by it; the fixed ends of the muscle approach one another, and so the two bones must take up another position with regard to one another. It is possible for one of the bones to be fixed and the other mobile, or both can be mobile. The return to the original position is caused by the contraction of the muscle on the opposite side of the joint.

This representation of the work done by the muscles is only an aid to a first rough comprehension of movement; the bones are lever arms which the muscles, as moving forces, grasp. Nevertheless, the method of expression, although it is in general use, easily produces the incorrect impression that one muscle moves the bone forward and the other brings it back. This is not so. In every movement all the muscles around the joint in question are active, although not all to the same extent; some bring about the movement (prime movers and synergic muscles), the others regulate and moderate it by their counter-effect (antagonist and fixation muscles). Of course this can only happen within the scope for movement of the joint, that is, within the limits set by the structure of the joint, and therefore, by the shape of the articular surfaces of the bones meeting there, the nature of the joint capsule and the ligaments strengthening it. These extra ligaments are often only found on one side of the joint, or are especially strongly developed there, and then they limit freedom of movement to a certain extent.

However, it is not enough to understand the movement in one single joint. The many joints in the body stand in a definite relationship to each other. For nearly every bone is part of two joints, so a movement in one of them is always continued in others. Thus one speaks of the 'remote effect' of muscles. This becomes very clear in the following example which was also used in Section I: if one asks somebody, with his arms hanging loosely by his side, to bend his elbow, the upper arm does not remain motionless in its place whilst the lower arm moves up to it—on the contrary, both upper and lower arm change their position; they move towards each other. So an uncalled-for movement takes place in the shoulder joint. It can be suppressed if one tries very hard, but then one can clearly feel a muscular tension which is not noticeable in the natural movement. When this happens the movement is no longer self-evident and unforced; nobody who performs this movement of his own accord does it in this manner (Figure 4).

This can be expressed differently and then it at once gains

significance for good posture. The whole arm, suspended from the shoulder joint and completely free to swing to and fro, represents a system which is in balance. If a change is made in this system, as here by bending the elbow, then unwilled changes follow the movement consciously willed; these lead to a new state of equilibrium—without them the centre of gravity would no longer be under the point of suspension. The lever arms of the human apparatus of movement do not, therefore, turn on axes which pass through the joints but on axes which pass through the centres of gravity of the individual parts of the body concerned in the movement; the joints merely form surfaces which guide the movement.

Figure 4. Bending the elbow whilst the arm is hanging down loosely. The upper arm goes back a little but by consciously flexing the muscles this 'remote effect' can be suppressed

So human movements are, mechanically, not such a simple matter as many people believe, but are a complicated interplay of conscious and unconscious processes. The cortex of the cerebrum alone cannot bring about co-ordinated movement; subcortical, phylogenetically older centres always take part. If they fail, severe disruption of the movement takes place—a proof of their importance. These indications must suffice; perhaps they will make the teacher who believes in precepts for movement reflect a little.

One can imagine the whole human body as a compound system of levers, supported at its centre of gravity. A movement, beginning in any part of it, must follow a definite course simply because of its structural plan and the necessity for a new position of equilibrium. A feeling for this defined course must be aroused in the pupil, he must learn to allow movements in the body to 'level out'. For a return to the position of equilibrium occurs as a reflex action, and can never be replaced by precepts for posture and movement, however ingenious. Herein lies the great danger of all precepts. In children especially many mistakes never occur at all if they are not called into being by incorrect precepts.

Movements carried out incorrectly—those in opposition to the structure of the body and the biological peculiarities of the apparatus of movement—prevent efficient movement and so harm achievement (properly conceived); and incorrect demands made continually on the body eventually disrupt it and thus also harm its form.

Only free, naturally performed movements, which exploit the wonderful efficiency of the body, result in a physical training which furthers form and achievement equally.

To judge the 'correct' execution of movements is not too difficult; the method which best conserves energy is the most efficient and thus also has the most beautiful form. Since with children one can luckily reckon on a certain measure of natural skill it is usually not at all difficult to achieve correct movements. One should tell the children what to do but not how to do it, this they will best discover for themselves. This is the easiest way to achieve beautiful movements.

(b) *The building up of posture*

Among the various positions of rest in man, standing upright is by far the most difficult. In movement the adjustment of the joints is continually changing; with every moment it is different but when the body is still, the joints have a definite adjustment, and on this the type of posture is based. It is the result of a quite definite state of equilibrium among the large muscle groups of the trunk, which gradually comes about in response to the nature of the demands made. Thus, standing upright can rightly be evaluated as a pointer to the physical state of the pupil. It allows a judgement to be made on the way the physical exercises are being carried out. Only a teacher who never loses his eye for the

Plate I

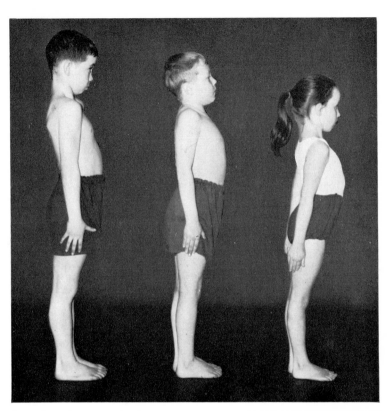

Standing 'to attention'

Plate II

Natural good posture

whole body and its natural form will achieve the even development of the muscles which brings about correctly adjusted
muscular pull, and so effects correct balance of all the parts over
the base.

First we will concern ourselves with the question of which
adjustment of the joints is the best in an upright body. From now
on this will be called 'build'.*

When the 'build' is correct the body gives the impression of
being at rest. As in a building the parts of the body rest upon
one another according to their weight; if the legs, trunk and
head are 'built up' correctly on one another, less muscular work
is needed to hold the position. For, as already described, that
mode of execution of a movement which uses least energy is the
most efficient and therefore most beautiful, so for 'build', that
adjustment which demands the least outlay of energy is clearly
the best. The muscles always have to do a certain amount of
work or else it is impossible to stand upright; the skeleton alone
would fall down. It is just a case of finding the position in which
the muscles do not have to do any more work than necessary.
If the parts of the skeleton are not placed one above the other,
the muscles, which already have to work against gravity to hold
the skeleton upright, have to do much more work. Further, the
muscles must not 'tug' at the skeleton and perhaps even force it
into a position which can only be described as a caricature, they
must bring it into a state of equilibrium and hold it there easily.
Plate I shows the unnatural posture, with the breathing disturbed, which used to result from imposing the military bearing
on children by asking them to 'stand to attention', in contrast to
the child's natural good posture in Plate II.

The best proof that it is not a question of strength itself but
of relationships of strength is the fact that physically weak people
quite often have good posture—or rather, are well 'built up',
whilst strong people can be very badly 'built up'. Too much
strength at any point is as disruptive as too little, on account of the
incorrect pull of the muscles. The total amount of strength is, of
course, of no importance at all in achieving a correct relationship
of strength.

As soon as one has realized that posture must be 'built up',

---

* Not to be confused with the usual meaning of the word in the context of human
physique—proportions of the body.

it is clear that one has of necessity to begin at the base. Anyone who is told to build a pillar, a tower, etc., out of children's bricks will make use of this principle without giving it special thought.

Careful work is absolutely essential if some of the bricks are much longer than they are broad, and if one has to work to a definite plan according to which the long bricks have to stand on their small surface. Then the building up has to be done extremely carefully, otherwise not even a small degree of stability is obtainable.

The whole mass of the construction must be piled up as regularly as possible, with the line of gravity as the axis: the centres of gravity of the individual bricks must lie perpendicularly above one another.

There is special difficulty in arranging the bricks round the line of gravity like this if they not only have a 'top' and a 'bottom' but also show a 'front' and a 'back'—if they are symmetrical on two sides only. Then the whole construction will have two matching halves—in it one can discern a right and left side, a front and a back. It is easy to build up the two matching sides; the difficulty consists in the correct adjustment of the two halves differing from one another; there one cannot so easily see the right way to distribute the weight.

Circumstances are exactly the same when it comes to building up the body; adjustment on the plane from right to left is much easier than that on the plane at right angles to it—from front to back. And indeed, adjustment from side to side does not even begin to present such difficulties, either to the intellect or in actual execution, as that from front to back, because the symmetry of the two halves gives an infallible standard. Because of this, lateral deformities have always been recognized and combated. These deformities will not be considered here, as their treatment is not a part of physical education in school; they demand special curative treatment.

Whilst every parent has a horror of a crooked back, it occurs to very few of them ever to look at a child's posture from the side. And yet the adjustment in this plane is of fundamental importance for the health and beauty of the body, not least because of its influence on the breathing, which will be discussed in more detail later.

Before discussing the subject in detail, we will first look briefly at the whole structure of the human body. The pelvis balances on the hip-joints, supported by the legs, and forms a base for the whole trunk. The spine is attached to the posterior rim of the pelvis and its lowest part is wedged immovably in the pelvis, so the spine must take part in all the movements of the pelvis. This explains the influence, often mentioned later, of the position of the pelvis on the adjustment of the spine. Reciprocally, the pelvis has to follow the movements of the trunk. From the pelvis the spine rises up, free and elastic, bearing the head on its top.

The thorax hangs on the middle part of the spine and forms a sort of protective box for the thoracic organs. On it rests the shoulder girdle which serves as a point of attachment for the arms.

This is the essential structure of the body; from it, it is easy to ascertain which factors are decisive for the upright position. They are: (i) the position of the pelvis, which carries the trunk; (ii) the elasticity and strength of the spine, which holds the body upright, and is the basic support of the upright position; (iii) the adjustment of the thorax over the pelvis, and a natural manner of breathing; and (iv) a good head position. When these four points have been attended to, the whole body should be right.

Now we will go into the essential structure of the body and its peculiarities in more detail. The pelvis rests in the two hip-joints on the legs, and is thus supported in only two places. One can imagine it as a bowl, not laid horizontally, but inclined so that the front edge lies lower than the back one. To determine the degree of pelvic inclination one takes the angle formed by the plane of the entrance to the pelvis with the horizontal: it varies between 55 and 75 degrees. When standing up the hip-joints are stretched to very nearly their full extent.

The pelvis may turn on both hip-joints together as if hinged on fulcra like angled levers (Figure 5); if the front arm of the lever is raised, the back goes down, and vice versa. It is possible for it to tilt backwards until the Bertinian ligaments which pass across the front of the hip-joints are fully extended and bring it up short. Forwards it can tilt to a practically unlimited extent. In all positions the pelvis is held and balanced by a series of large muscles which run obliquely from the pelvis to the legs and bring about the various movements in the hip-joints.

As is well known the spinal column is made up of many bones, the vertebrae, which are connected with one another by the vertebral discs and by joints. Although the individual vertebrae do not move very much in relation to one another, the sum of their small movements produces a very considerable flexibility of the spinal column as a whole.

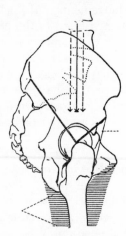

Figure 5.
The pelvis
as an angled lever
(after Braus)

The spinal discs represent about a quarter of the length of the spine. They are so constructed (a gelatinous centre which can be shifted within a fibrous ring) that they work like rubber buffers. They make the spinal column an elastic structure, especially as it also has elastic ligaments running along it which, in any position but the upright one, are stretched and so are always striving to bring the spine back to the upright position. These support the extended position, and thus conserve muscular power.

This elastic column, that holds the trunk upright, does not rise straight up from the pelvis; when one looks at it from the side it reveals three curves—in the lumbar and cervical regions the curve is forwards, in the thoracic region it is backwards. When standing up these curves can, to a certain extent, be voluntarily increased or diminished but they can never be quite eliminated. They are closely dependent on each other: the consequence of any increase in one of them is an increase in the others. This is easy to explain, for as we mentioned earlier, the distribution of weight about the line of gravity must be even. So, if one point is pushed out of the line of gravity, one on the opposite side must be pushed out of it to the same extent; a stronger curve in one part must be compensated for by increasing the curve in the part adjacent to it. Thus, for example, an increased hollowing of the lumbar region, the so-called hollow back, must be compensated for by a greater arching of the thoracic part.

The double S curve of the spine is a result of man's standing upright. Throughout the period of growth, until about the seventeenth year, changes are still continually taking place in the spine until eventually its final form is attained.

The curves in the spinal column protect the head from the jolts which would otherwise disturb it when walking, running, or jumping.

When the spine is well extended a man is as tall as he ever can be. If he does not hold his head as high as possible the curves in the spine become greater.

The spine is held upright by the long back muscles; these prevent the trunk from falling over. They spring from the pelvis, and, attaching themselves to individual vertebrae, continue up to the head. When the body is bent slowly forwards and downwards it is these muscles that hold the body against gravity and that raise it up again.

The thorax is attached to the middle part of the spine. This box, which protects the vital organs of the chest, lessens the ability to move this region, for there is no movement of the pectoral part of the spine in which the thorax does not take part.

The thorax is, like the spinal column, an elastic structure which is always striving to remain in a position of equilibrium. In contrast to the pelvis, which is quite firm, the thorax of a living person is continually moving to and fro, and is thus never rigid. Like the pelvis, the whole thorax can be tilted on a frontal axis, and it can be pushed forward so that it no longer hangs over the pelvis. It can also be 'opened out' by spreading the ribs 'like a fan'.

On the thorax rests the shoulder girdle, which is the point of contact between the arms and the trunk. Only in front is it connected to the skeleton by joints, at the back it is 'open' and connected to the trunk solely by muscles. When the spinal column is kept well extended, the head held high, and the thorax well developed, the shoulders take up the right position quite by themselves as, yielding to their own weight, they rest on the thorax. Pulling the shoulder-blades back with the muscles is a valuable exercise but not the correct adjustment for just standing up. This is to be achieved only by correctly adjusting the thorax on which the shoulder-blades 'float', and therefore only by correctly adjusting the spinal column to which the thorax is attached.

In the skeleton a 'window' is visible between the pelvis and the thorax; in the living man it is filled in with a bridge of muscles made out of three belts: the abdominal wall. These abdominal muscles take part in every movement of the trunk, also in the movements of the pelvis in relation to the legs. The abdominal muscles also bring the pelvis and the thorax towards one another, and rotate them in opposition to one another. They hold the intestines in place, and are, in breathing, an important counterpart to the diaphragm.

(a) *Errors in 'build'*

The upright position of man is, like speech and the prehensile hand, phylogenetically a comparatively recent acquisition. Every individual must acquire it anew, and must continually maintain it in face of threats. In addition to this there are the harmful effects of civilization brought about by incorrect clothing and shoes, one-sided professional work, etc. For the schoolchild the harm done by having to sit far too much of the time must be mentioned before all else. The following are some of the commoner postural faults.

(i) When the tilt of the pelvis is increased into a 'steep' position (Plate III, two positions of the pelvis) the sacrum is more sharply inclined forwards, the angle between the sacrum and the lumbar region of the spinal column becomes smaller, and the lumbar curve more pronounced; to compensate for this a bigger curve results in the pectoral region, and this in turn brings about an increased curve in the neck.

An example of the steep position of the pelvis is given by the statue of 'Salome' of E. Seeger. When one compares it with the famous 'Venus de Milo' the determinative influence of the

Plate III

Two positions of the pelvis

Plate IV

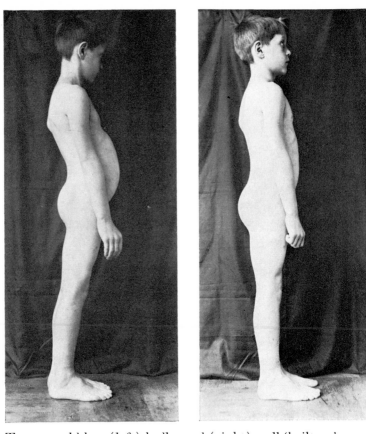

Ten year old boy (left) badly, and (right) well 'built-up'

pelvic position on the whole configuration of the trunk becomes very clear.

The harmfulness of habitual steep inclination of the pelvis is firstly contained in the fact that this presses the weight of the intestines too strongly forward against the abdominal wall and stretches it. When this is continually stretched its tension is reduced. Quite apart from its ugliness, the fault is very harmful both to correct breathing and to the retention of the abdominal organs in their correct position.

Another harmful consequence can be seen in the thorax. When the spinal column is well extended the thorax can be carried free and high without any special exertion; when the part of the spine on which it hangs is more curved it too sinks down; the apices of the lungs are then in a particularly unfavourable position.

(ii) Another very common postural fault in children, especially in those with weak muscles, is that the legs, instead of being perpendicular, incline forwards (Plate IV). The consequences are plainly to be seen in the line of the back and the line from abdomen to chest. To compensate, the body has to lean backwards and the spine forms a shallow curve, beginning quite far down.

(iii) Besides the steep positioning of the pelvis and the pushing forward of the hips, a reduction of the pelvic tilt can also be the reason for a postural fault. This limits the lumbar hollow to the very bottom part of the spine, and the thoracic curve begins too far down. In this postural fault, round shoulders occur, and it is very obvious how the head is poked forward and the chest caves in.

One can see that the pelvis, as the base of the trunk, determines posture. It would be senseless to busy oneself with the spine or the thorax whilst allowing the cause, that is the incorrect position of the pelvis, to remain.

(iv) It is also a fault if the thorax is not held elastically over the pelvis but is pushed forward, or if it is turned upon a frontal axis instead of being opened out—a fault which very often came into being in response to the order 'chests out!'.

(v) Another very common fault is that the shoulder blades are poked forwards. A shortening of the pectoral muscles is both the cause and the effect of this.

A few more words are necessary on the origination of faults in the 'build'. Little children usually have not yet acquired a firm posture with the stamp of their personality upon it such as we are used to seeing in adults. They stand now this way, now that— usually they do not stand still at all—today they have this fault, tomorrow that. Their posture is not firm. The bigger the children grow the more they tend to adopt the same posture again and again when they stand. If this is bad, then habit makes it more and more pronounced. For when the adjustment is continually incorrect, changes come about in the muscles, the joint casings, and the ligaments (lengthening on one side, shortening on the other). Their incorrect pull makes the incorrect joint position even worse and this in turn works to further the contraction or lengthening of the muscles and ligaments, and a vicious circle is formed the consequence of which appears as a definite postural fault.

(b) *Exercises of adjustment and 'build'*
The aim of posture exercises is the correct adjustment of the skeleton. This must be maintained or, if it has been lost, restored; and it must be brought into the pupil's consciousness. The adjustment of the skeleton depends on the pull of the muscles which are attached to it, especially in the trunk. If the posture is to be changed these muscles have, so to speak, to learn to pull differently. Of course, all exercises with this aim can be carried out only by the energy of the muscles, but their purpose is not to strengthen the muscles; they apply not to the muscles but to the nerves, more properly the nervous system which regulates muscle action.

Plate IV shows this very clearly. The picture on the right was taken only a few minutes after the one on the left. In this length of time no physical fault, as for example a shortening of the muscles, could have been cured; this, according to the theory of functional adaptation (Lange, W., 1917), takes at least thirty days (unit of adaptation). The obvious improvement in posture can thus proceed only from a changed muscular pull, that is, better co-operation of the muscles, resulting from a different co-ordination which has somehow been imparted to the boy. This quick, sometimes instantaneous effect shows a clear difference from all corrective exercises which need time to take effect.

These co-ordinating exercises have been greatly undervalued in posture education, but they serve the important purpose of encouraging the pupil to sense minor adjustments in his own body and so find for himself the best posture.

These exercises can be put together under the heading: exercises of adjustment and 'build', of which the 'build up' exercises are a special group, performed in the standing position.

They are posture exercises in the narrowest sense of the word; their aim is to teach the pupil doing them to 'feel' what position and place the parts of his body adopt with reference to one another; his feeling for his body must be developed, and it is not his sense of sight but muscular feeling which must make him conscious of each new adjustment. This feeling for the body can be made very much more delicate with practice.

It is best to undertake these exercises in such a way that one first makes the pupil adopt the incorrect position and then makes him change with slow, calm movements to the correct one. Jerky, sudden movements are forbidden here, as it is always a matter of delicate adjustment with relatively small displacements; only when one follows carefully the course of the movement can one find the correct point at which to stop; beyond this point one falls into the opposite fault. So one hovers around the position of equilibrium like a pair of scales when it is not 'arrested'. This is the best image for preventing both teacher and pupil from adopting an incorrect position.

First they are undertaken for the adjustment of individual joints (e.g. hip-joint) or parts (e.g. spine), and as far as possible in a position in which movement is restricted in all other joints, so that the pupil can concentrate his whole attention on the adjustment of the one joint.

In these exercises no account is taken of the perpendicular position. For example, the adjustment of the lumber region can be practised in a crouching position in order to make the pupil conscious of the capabilities for movement in this region. However, this does not mean that he is capable of adjusting the lumbar region correctly when he is standing up.

In the 'build up' exercises too which, as mentioned, aim at achieving correct adjustment in the upright position, one often proceeds by stages, e.g., by first attending only to the position of the foot joints. The 'build up' must always begin at the base; a higher joint must never be put right until all those below it have been settled, otherwise faults are unavoidable.

As the feeling for the body grows, more and more joints can be included in the exercise, until finally the whole 'build up' of the standing position has been achieved.

Teaching good posture is easy to discuss but difficult to carry out. It is the intention of this essay to emphasize some aspects of the posture problem.

Good posture in sitting and standing indicates a position of equilibrium which can be reached only by 'levelling out' into it. The human body rests in the two hip-joints on the legs, the centre of gravity lies over the point of support and sinks when movement begins. In the upright position stable equilibrium can never be reached. One therefore has to learn to come to terms with an unstable equilibrium. Over and over again the muscles have to seize the various parts of the skeleton and bring them over the surface of support. A body which is relatively tall and possesses only a small surface on which it is supported, cannot attain any high degree of stability—much less if it consists of parts which do not, it is true, fall apart but which can be mutually displaced. When they rest exactly above one another they rest, as a result of gravity, on one another. If one part is displaced from the perpendicular, one of the parts lying above it must be displaced in the opposite direction in order to maintain a state of balance. The smaller the surface on which the whole is supported the more exactly must the parts be placed one upon another, that is the 'build up' must be more accurate. This is incidentally the reason why turning the feet outwards, which increases the area of the supporting base, is not helpful for achieving good posture, because one cannot do much in this direction, and because it changes nothing of importance in the unstable equilibrium. The way of tackling the continual threat to our balance is not to increase the area of the supporting base, but it lies in the readiness to move one's point of support to another place and 'build up' again on the new one.

One can thus recognize good posture from the fact that the body is 'built up' as much as possible in a perpendicular line, neither the hips nor the thorax departing from the perpendicular axis.

From this it can also be understood that a part of teaching

good posture is to accustom the children to stand with their feet together and not get into the habit of standing with their feet apart. One should experiment for oneself how much more easily the hips are displaced sideways if the legs are straddled than if they are kept together. From this can be seen the value, when teaching good posture to children, of having them practise standing on tip-toe.

From what we have already said it is clear that the lower a joint lies in the body the more important it is for good posture, for the joints are the places at which all displacement happens. It was therefore basically incorrect for people always to seek good posture 'at the top', as the posture precept 'chest out, shoulders back' demands. Of course one must attend to the joints at the top too, but only when one is sure that those below them are correct.

Further, the position of equilibrium can be reached only by 'levelling out' into it, not by becoming rigid. If one arrests the movement of a pair of scales it no longer acts like a pair of scales. The person concerned must learn to feel when he has reached the position of equilibrium; one can see this from outside only if one has had great practice in looking for it. In consequence of this, good posture must always be free, never forced, tense or rigid.

Various scientific reasons could be introduced in justification of this requirement. Here we will discuss three of them, so that in one place at least an explanation is given of why these requirements are not arbitrary but well-founded. First: good posture has to be adopted for ever, not just for a few minutes when the teacher happens to ask for it. The goal is for the pupil always to stand and to move well. This is only possible if good posture is so constituted as not to impede the breathing; this needs no further justification. The breathing is a delicate movement which continually dilates and contracts the thorax. Any rigidity disturbs it. Indeed, one often sees that people with tense 'good posture' give it up after a short while with a deep sigh—a sure sign that they find their breathing impeded and disturbed. Second: the spine, the prop of the body, has a form peculiar to it to which it strives elastically to return. The vertebrae are connected by elastic discs which work like rubber cushions, and thus attempt to force the vertebrae back into their position of rest. If one purposely adopts a tense posture one impedes the play of the elastic forces in the spine. And the third thing: we now know what a large influence the position of the head has on the distribution of tension in the muscles of the limbs and trunk. From the position of the head in relation to the body, and from the position of the head in space, reflexes proceed and thus movements are produced. In a rigid posture these movements become impossible, the reflexes cannot work themselves out. It would certainly be very presumptuous to think that man could replace the effect of something like the reflexes by intellectual activity! So the demand that good posture should be free is well founded; but this is exactly the point which always raises the most doubts.

One scarcely needs to discuss in detail the value to health of good posture. The trunk is a receptacle for the vital organs—heart, lungs, etc.; it safeguards their natural position and thus their correct functioning. The connection between bad posture and breathing and a tendency to pulmonary tuberculosis is probably familiar enough. And the expression, known even to the layman, of 'displacement' clearly indicates the importance of the correct positioning of the organs. The harmful effect of high heels is based, among other things, on the fact that they put the feet, and therefore the legs, and therefore the pelvis, in a position other than the natural one, and the relations of the internal organs to each other are thus altered. One must not forget that the upright position of man is phylogenetically a recent acquisition and thus continually endangered, so that it is necessary to take care of it.

On what then does good posture depend? On everything really! It is a pointer to the physical state of a person at any given time. Friedel (1930) wrote an article on the connection between breathing through one's nose and the development of the thorax, a connection which had already been pointed out by the Rotenburger Schule (see glossary, *Gymnastik*). A woman, Dr Hörnicke (1925), demonstrated that there is a fundamental connection between clothes and types of breathing; in 1930 a physiological work (Okunewa, Steinbach and Schtscheglowa) established a connection between a kind of physical work—carrying weights—and the type of breathing. Since posture is to a great extent determined by breathing one can say that all the factors named affect posture. Or think of the effect of a bolster on someone who habitually sleeps on his back! The head is pushed forward (think of the person lying down as if he had been stood on end) and this happens for about a third of his life. This cannot be without effect on his posture. Correct skin-care, food, etc., also have an effect, even if it cannot be shown in detail. In order to foster good posture the school must also concern itself with these things and, since it cannot do everything on its own, must try to win the co-operation of the home.

10   *Posture exercises*

Now for the question of most importance for us: what must physical education do? All the prerequisites are of the utmost importance but they alone do not assure one of good posture. It is something which must be won, it only falls of its own accord to a few very lucky people. It is not an assured possession, in the highest sense, until it is conscious; once it has been recognized as a value it cannot be lost. In this physical education must help.

One must judge all exercises undertaken by the pupils according to their effect on posture. All exercises which do not stand up to this test must be eliminated. For example, the popular exercises like the 'crows-nest', the 'crab', etc., which force the body into an arch with the abdominal wall stretched and an exaggerated curve in the lumber spine are by no means harmless to posture, at least for children with weak posture (Spitzy, 1926). The curve naturally takes effect on the weakest part, as a staff which one bends too far breaks at its weakest point; the weakest part of the spine is the lumbar region. As it is, we have enough trouble strengthening the bridge of muscles from pelvis to thorax and obtaining sufficient muscle tone in this area. Such exercises should therefore be eradicated from gymnastics.

Then school gymnastic lessons must be so planned that they contain enough movement of the trunk. Previously pure limb movements were unduly preferred in gymnastics.

It must still be emphasized that much body work is needed such as is provided by, for example, pulling, throwing, climbing and many jumps, above all twisting jumps and crouch jumps.

Besides these we do special exercises of the trunk which are intended in a short time to work thoroughly and strengthen the bodies of all the pupils. These exercises of the trunk must be spacious; they must not be geometrical, i.e. using only the three planes which we place in space as aids to thought, but must use all the others as well. So all circling of the arms is more valuable

than raising and dropping them, twisting and bending the
body is better than merely bending forwards and sideways; in short all curved or spiral movements are of more
value than the straight ones.

Only on the foundation of such general, indirect care of
posture has direct posture education any meaning or success.
One must observe a very carefully thought-out methodical
procedure; above all one must know that age-level plays a
decisive role in its framing, since one has to reckon on the
intellectual co-operation of the pupils and this can be expected
only when they have reached a certain stage of development.
The basic thought must be that upright posture is present in the
child just as the striving to grow upwards lies in the plant. This
process of growing upright can be hindered by all kinds of
extraneous influences. The hindrances must therefore be
removed, and at a certain level of development the child must
become aware of what has been vividly called the 'buttressing
force'. Such hindrances often lie in bad postural habits; if, for
example, someone continually keeps his arms crossed, the
buttressing force cannot take effect.
Primary schools must educate the child to good postural
habits.

One of the most important things is standing with the feet
close together and straight, the weight kept more on the
toes than the heels.

Also one must stand so that by inclining the head
forward one can see one's feet (this makes sure that the
hips are not pushed forward); the head must be held
high (as every child understands), the breath must not be
held, and the arms must hang down loosely.

These simple, perceptible things can be understood without
any difficulty by the children once they have been pointed out to
them; they can easily see them. Special practising is scarcely
necessary; one explains the point, makes the children watch, and
reminds them when they forget again. One habituates them to it
just as one habituates them to washing their hands before a
meal; this is not specially practised either but is supervised until
they do it of their own accord.

In every gymnastic lesson in the primary school there is an unforced opportunity to remind the children of good posture; for example, when they are doing a balance-step, remind them to hold their heads up, or when they are sitting tell them in a little pause to sit up straight. One must work continually at posture; the children must feel that the teacher never forgets that he wants their posture to be good. If one only thinks and speaks about it oneself once a year nothing will be attained. Success here does not depend on special, new, original exercises but on the constancy with which one considers posture whatever exercise one may be doing.

In the secondary school this education must be continued and broadened. Many postural precepts will be discussed again because they can now be more deeply and forcibly explained. More than in the primary school one will have to make use of corrective exercises against harm done by too much sitting, and against posture faults which appear as a result of the growth in height during puberty.

In addition, the pupils will now be made to do special posture exercises, which are introduced to them as such. They are based on the swinging on a central point which becomes smaller and smaller until the position of equilibrium is reached (bending the head forwards and backwards). In this the image of the scales helps again and again. Or one consciously leaves one position of equilibrium and looks for another on a new support, as, for example, happens in the falling exercises (see above p. 19). It is always delicate movements, small displacements in the body, or finely intercepted, gently elastic movements which lead to a new position of equilibrium. The following are examples of posture exercises.

> The weight must rest on the centre of the feet. To learn this one stands upright and displaces one's weight first as far forwards and then as far backwards as possible (Figure 6), and whilst swaying to and fro one discovers the central point between the two limits. Physics, which provides the concept of the line of gravity, can further help the children to understand this. One can also practise swaying from side to side, and circling without moving the feet. In these exercises one must gradually bring

about a full extension of the knee and hip-joints, which will then also be called for when the pupil stands still.

The possibility of positioning the thorax in various ways over the pelvis is best tried out in a sitting position with the knees drawn up in front, the various ways of circling the body whilst sitting are used here. Gentle little movements to and fro allow one to discover the position in which the thorax hovers over the pelvis. The feeling for this must then be found in a standing position too. Finally, one must also see that the shoulders are not hunched up.

All work on the chest and shoulder region brings with it a danger of impeding the breathing, and of an incorrect beginning of inspiration. One must therefore, carefully harmonize these posture exercises with the breathing. Also one must give the

Figure 6. Swaying forwards and backwards keeping the feet still

pupil the insight, which up to now has been a guide only to the teacher, that our posture is always a position of equilibrium and never a fixed one; that it is always free to change, and this makes completely unimpeded breathing possible even when one is fully extended. The image of the scales which has been used with the children mainly to depict the 'levelling out' now becomes a precept for all posture exercises. Such special posture exercises are included in the first part of the lesson or at the end. Reminders about good posture belong everywhere in the lesson where they are found to be necessary.

The teacher must never forget that a child who does not get the necessary amount of movement will never have good posture; it cannot be imparted to him by even the best 'posture exercises'. This cannot be said plainly enough. Posture exercises are described in such detail because this is necessary in order to make the principles of natural posture training clear to the teacher, and give him the knowledge which is essential if he is to work on the posture of children. However, he must take care not to try to spend the children's gymnastic lessons wholly or mainly on posture exercises. The general playing activity of children cannot be replaced by anything else. It alone creates harmonious development.

Although all the growth processes which lead to the final form of the body and to posture with a personal stamp are not yet completed, posture training must be completed by the time compulsory schooling ends. The pupil must know these decisive factors so well that it is impossible for him ever to forget them, only then is he sure of taking good posture as a possession into life with him.

Corrective exercises are one of the most difficult and controversial fields in physical education. Even as regards theory we are not yet in complete agreement about them and many problems are still unsolved. It is thus not easy to find the right way in practical work.

What, in the first place, are corrective exercises? We have Gaulhofer to thank for a clear definition of the concept. He distinguishes between four large groups of exercises, classified according to the aim of the teacher: (i) Corrective exercises, the purpose of which is to remove or correct faults in the structure of the body. (ii) Formative exercises (see glossary), by means of which the best personal form of movement and posture is to be attained. (iii) Exercises of achievement, with which one tries to increase the capabilities of the individual to his greatest level of achievement. (iv) Artistic movement, by means of which the desire for movement is to be turned into a beautiful and artistic game with movement.

Corrective exercises are therefore supposed to remove, or at least reduce, faults in the structure of the body. Such faults are: (i) insufficient scope for movement in a joint, i.e., below average mobility (exercises to correct this are called exercises in flexibility); (ii) too much muscular tension (loosening exercises serve to combat this) and (iii) special weakness of certain groups of muscles (against this, compensatory strengthening exercises are used).

In order to decide how the exercises must be framed so that they really do fulfil their purpose one must possess an abundant and deep knowledge of the human apparatus for movement. Otherwise it can easily happen that, with the best intentions and honest conviction, one does exercises which cannot bring about the desired effect and may perhaps even have the opposite one. Under certain circumstances one can do more harm than good; at the very least one is wasting time.

The following is one example out of the many that are possible. In literature on gymnastics one finds exercises for stretching the pectoral muscles. In a position which restricts movement in certain joints, or with the aid of a helper, a pull is exerted on the pectoral muscles; the person doing the exercise is thus brought into a position which he would not be able to adopt by himself. This, so one thinks, will stretch the pectoral muscles and they will become longer. Certainly this can be the case, but only under certain conditions. In the first place the exercises must be done very gently, not at all violently—otherwise exactly the opposite occurs: the muscles 'defend themselves', they contract even more strongly by reflex action and do not yield. As long as the muscles do not let go they cannot be stretched, furthermore, the movement cannot go beyond the utmost bounds of the respective joint or complex of joints (as in the spine), and in any case these exercises must be done often and for a long time. Orthopaedists wishing to stretch the muscles of a recumbent patient by the pull of weights make the patient lie down up to three times daily, each time for from a quarter to half an hour (Lange, F., 1928). From this one can see at once that very little can be achieved in two to three weekly periods of exercise, which in any case cannot be used for stretching exercises alone. If such exercises in these positions of restricted movement or with a helper are carried out, it is for quite different reasons. Through them the pupil experiences— intuitively of course, not intellectually—that it is possible to move thus far in this joint. The method of teaching is the same as when one makes a child, who cannot hit on the right moment to 'jump into' the circling skipping-rope, stand between two who can do it well: they pull the child with them, and he gradually learns how to do it intuitively.

So one can see that the application of corrective exercises is not such a simple matter.

Should one then do no corrective exercises at all in gymnastic lessons? Or has one or other of the three groups named a general application? In fact it is the exercises in flexibility against whose general use one must be warned most particularly, since they not only waste time but can actually do harm. Loosening exercises are not completely harmless because—especially in city children—there tends to be too great slackness in the muscles in any case and because one too easily considers loosening as a goal in itself, whereas it can only ever be a step towards a further goal. As exercises to be included generally, the compensatory strengthening exercises are of most use and they can scarcely do any harm.

Corrective exercises can be applied only when the faults they are meant to combat are really present. This also means that they must be framed as much as possible to suit the individual, they are not of much use as mass exercises, apart from a few which correct universal faults. This will be further discussed later.

How then does one know that a fault is present? Fully developed faults, as for example round shoulders or a slack abdomen, are of course easily ascertainable for they are directly visible. Yet, in school children especially, it is often a case of faults which are only just developing, and which cannot so easily be seen from outside. They appear only when the body is called upon to do various things which they somehow 'impede'. Thus weak abdominal muscles prevent the performance of an upward circle on the bar; stiffness in the hip-joints hinders a good fence vault, etc. This means that one cannot judge whether faults are coming into being from pupils who are standing still—in this position only big, fully developed faults can be seen—but only after one has watched them for a long time doing all sorts of different exercises.

Furthermore, it is an established fact that many faults disappear 'by themselves', that is without doing specific exercises to correct them, if the pupils are given opportunity for profitable, varied movement. The principle of total movement is now a teaching principle generally accepted, at least in theory. Exercises which make use of the whole body (not just small parts of it, as for example the arms) use the faulty parts as well—and this corrects a good deal; developing faults are nipped in the bud. Thus exercises which are not corrective exercises, in that they have not been invented to correct faults, can have a compensatory effect. For example, walking with very long strides makes the hip-joints more flexible, as does crawling under a low rope, without one being able on this account to call these exercises 'exercises in flexibility'. Some exercises on the other hand have the effect of producing faults, e.g., the back bends, still so popular, increase the slackness of the abdominal muscles.

The following points must be considered with regard to the battle against faults: all exercises used in gymnastics must also be judged according to their corrective effect. Exercises which produce faults must not be done, even when they are valuable in other respects or have been hallowed by centuries of tradition. Exercises which correct some fault and have therefore a compensatory effect ought to be increased in number as soon as the fault in question is noticed. The correction of faults is thus a teaching principle not honoured only by the use of corrective exercises.

A comparison taken from everyday life is well suited to show the importance of corrective exercises: if one wants to clean a cooking utensil one first washes it as a whole, and only after this does one work with an abrasive or with a cleanser on the places which have not become clean. Only then does one see where the spot is which does not yield to washing; it can be removed only by increased work on it.

Applied to physical faults this means: only after general, varied work and only through this does one see where the faults lie; only at these points has work with specific corrective exercises any meaning. If there are no 'spots' one will not apply a 'cleanser' for this would only wear the utensil away unnecessarily.

This example can be carried further: one knows in advance, from the uses to which a cooking utensil is put, where extra care will be needed in washing up. Thus a utensil standing on an open flame will be black outside and will need specially careful cleansing. Or when a utensil is dented, dirt will catch there and will have to be scoured. With our school children too one knows in advance that faults are to be expected at certain points rather than at others. These are the weak points, so-called, of the body, at which faults can be observed in practically all children. So there will be a few corrective exercises which can generally be used for all classes and for all the children in a class.

Such weak points result on the one hand from the peculiar build of man, from the statical difficulties of his upright posture; on the other hand from the 'profession' of the school children, from their sitting in school. Such weak points are: the foot, the bridge of muscles between pelvis and thorax, the shoulder girdle.

In gymnastics the following corrective exercises are therefore valuable:

> All exercises which entail rising onto the toes, such as rocking on the feet, standing and walking on tip-toe, hopping and jumping, skipping, etc.; these strengthen the foot muscles.
>
> All exercises of the abdominal muscles such as sitting up from a recumbent position and raising and lowering the legs whilst lying on one's back; all exercises which swing the body round.
>
> All exercises which pull back the shoulders, therefore circling the arms in the shape of a funnel, drawing the arms back horizontally, 'bouncing' the arms backwards whilst sitting, preferably with the knees drawn up in front to restrict movement in the hip-joints and the lumbar spine.

There are many exercises based on the examples given here.

This almost exhausts the stock of corrective exercises which are of general use. All other corrective exercises belong only to special gymnastics working with small groups of pupils, treating them as individuals, and framed under the continual advice of a doctor, but which can be led by a teacher as long as he has gone into questions of physical education in some detail. Corrective exercises occupy a border-line position between ordinary gymnastics and remedial gymnastics. Anyone not quite sure of his subject would do better to leave them alone!

12   *Exercises of the trunk*

Exercises of the trunk form an important and indispensable constituent of the gymnastic lesson. They have two tasks to fulfil. On the one hand, they present an opportunity for the pupils (even those who are clumsy and take no pleasure in exercising) to exercise the whole body in a short period of time without any long preparation. On the other they will lead the pupils to work on improving their posture and movement. They are not exercises which proceed naturally from pleasure in movement and joy at one's own ability; they are a product of conscious education. They are aids to self-education, and not so much physical as intellectual aids. One must not think that good posture and movement can be attained through them alone but they can make the pupils conscious of everything that has already been learnt through movement experience in corporate work, and make it into a firm possession. All the work done in the gymnastic lesson must be framed according to good principles of form; exercises which are harmful to posture or movement must be omitted, however generally used they may be, however hallowed by tradition, or however modern. Only if this principle is followed can exercises of the trunk help to awake in the pupils an understanding of good posture and movement, so that they know what is required of them and thereby their co-operation is gained.

The execution of exercises of the trunk (repetition, number, etc.,) depends on whether one is aiming at a first general exercising, or at careful work to improve posture and movement. In the first case one will make the pupils do a great number of very varied exercises, in a surge of enthusiasm; in the second, one makes the pupils work carefully and in their own time at only a few exercises; then these are less a means of giving physical exercise—which must be provided in the rest of the lesson— than intellectual aids. The exercises of the trunk should never be prolonged until they seem to be the main part of the lesson; one must not think that everything can be achieved by means of exercises of the trunk; they are one of the many means available for forming the body and are effective only if used in conjunction with the others.

Originally by exercises of the trunk one meant isolated movements—that is, movements in one or a few joints—which are not the result of some visualized goal but of knowledge about a position to be reached or a movement to be done; for example, raising the arms forwards and upwards, putting a leg forward, bending the trunk sideways, etc. Such partial movements (see glossary) are not wholly to be avoided but they must not form the main body of the exercises of the trunk. Total movements, which proceed as a unity, are of much more importance. Examples of these are:

> Taking as long a step as possible forwards, sideways, or backwards; twisting the body when jumping; kneeling down without moving the feet from the ground; turning to front lying from a sitting position with the legs stretched; turning from back lying to front lying; getting up from back lying without the help of the hands; swinging the legs from side to side whilst sitting on a bench.
>
> Pushing back to back in pairs, that is against resistance; picking up and putting down objects, pushing them away and fetching them again, whilst standing, kneeling or sitting; rolling, throwing and catching or bouncing balls.
>
> Crawling along definite paths, for example, round skittles; climbing over or slipping through obstacles; hopping and jumping, also with twists, forwards, backwards and sideways.

There are countless such total movements and they are of much higher value for work on the trunk (exercises for flexibility, strengthening and co-ordination) than the arm and leg movements which used to be done. They force the pupils to make full use of the scope for movement in the joints, and they make varied demands on the muscles because they do not take place on one plane only. The fibrous parts of the muscles of the trunk are not arranged in parallel lines one above the other but often radiate from a central point. If the movements are executed only in straight lines, not all the fibres, but only those on the plane concerned, are forced to do productive work. And the most important muscles of the trunk are not just arranged along and across the body but in oblique directions too; so straight, geometrically combined movements are not sufficient for really radical work. We thus arrive at two requirements: not the isolated or partial movements but the total movements are to be emphasized; not the straight, geometrical movements but the curved, spiral ones are to be preferred in exercises of the trunk.

Total movements are always movements of a functional kind, they result from the unified co-operation of the muscles and are never limited to one joint but include all the joints in the section of the body used—arms, trunk or whole body. The movements do not stop abruptly but the body comes to rest gradually ending in a position of rest, such as sitting or lying. They are always concerned with external matters: a physically comprehensible task is described to the pupil and he tries to accomplish it without thinking of the actual movements necessary for this. The movement does not spring from his intellect only but, as is always the case in 'real' movements, from his feeling for movement or whatever one likes to call it. In other words, every intentional movement is guided by cortical impulses as well as by subcortical ones.

In carrying out these activities one can gradually habituate the children to good movement form by first teaching them to attend to easily perceptible things, such as everything they can see and hear. The command to jump down softly makes the landing elastic; the effort to catch a ball inaudibly leads them to reach out for it and follow its movement yieldingly with the arms; keeping the mouth closed decidedly improves the breathing.

Thus one can, in a delicate careful way which does not disturb the child's movement, awake a sense of the fact that movements can be done well and that it is worth while to make an effort for good form.

In this effort for good form of posture and movement, partial movements can be an effective aid. Teaching part of an activity is not in itself bad but care must be taken not to make use of partial movements too early and not in too great profusion; they must constitute only a small, well-considered part of the exercises in a gymnastic lesson and must be dedicated to improving posture and movement. They must never be material for arbitrary combinations of movements just for show.

Exercises which contribute to good form in movement are exercises which are intended to improve the interplay of the muscles, that is their co-ordination. Corrective exercises which lessen or remove faults create the conditions for good posture and movement but they do not produce these. The improvement in co-ordination occurs by attending to certain details in the execution of an activity, for example, to the amount of strength, or to relations in time (earlier, later) or space (direction, forwards, backwards, sideways, upwards, etc.), or to the accent in the course of a movement.

Only whole activities can be 'shaped'; with them alone is an objective judgement of good and bad possible. The partial movements must serve the same purpose as the whole activity, they must 'harmonize' with it. So the teacher learns the rules governing the execution of partial movements from the activities to which they belong, and for the improvement of which he is prescribing them.

The following example will explain how partial movements can be sensibly applied in a lesson. Crouch jump over a rope is an important exercise for developing the ability to spring. There are always some children who lift their point of gravity high enough over the rope or lath but do not bring their feet up far enough and so 'catch'. They are told how important it is to lift their feet up, and that they should watch the other pupils to see who does it well and who does not. Then in the exercises of the trunk they experiment to see how high the knee can be lifted; it is practised 'as high as possible', at first comfortably with the help of the hands, and later with more and more energetic lifting of the legs, alternately right and left. They practise raising both knees together whilst lying on their backs and also whilst hanging by the hands and arms. Next they do the crouch jump taking off from both feet and it does not matter where the take-off is because there is no rope over which the flight curve must be correctly executed. Finally, of course, they return to the lath or rope. Between whiles too there are frequent jumps over the rope when they can see how far the pulling up of the knees following on the run-up and take-off is successful.

In this process the child is fully aware why and for what purpose he is working at lifting up his knees. Behind it lies the goal he himself wishes to reach of getting higher and higher over the rope. He is therefore willing to practise since it is not a case of doing apparently senseless exercises.

Total movements cannot achieve everything in physical education. Posture training for example cannot be effectively helped on by total movements. Nevertheless for the general exercising of the trunk which should be given in the primary school, and for movement training, that is for teaching fluent, economical movement, they are of great value, and are in any case far superior to the separate exercises for arms, legs and trunk used in the past.

13　*Training correct breathing and breathing exercises*

The questions raised by training correct breathing are rather enveloped in mystery. Everyone feels that breathing is not something purely physical and is linked with the mystery of the mind. Acquaintance with the teachings of Yoga in particular has spread such ideas.

However, this must not lead either to the spread of obscure and esoteric doctrine in the field of training correct breathing nor to leaving the breathing to take care of itself out of fear of making mistakes. Carefully and cautiously all the important knowledge which we owe on the one hand to scientists like Durig (1931) and Hofbauer (1921), and on the other to the 'modern gymnastic systems' (see glossary, *Gymnastik*), must be built into physical education. This leads gradually to simple, clear rules for correct breathing which will be of help to all teachers.

It is probably generally known in professional circles that one has to distinguish sharply between exercises of the lungs and breathing exercises. 'Exercises of the lungs' include all those exercises in which one is unavoidably forced, by an increase of movement, to breathe more quickly and more deeply. From the point of view of method the lung exercises are the exercises of achievement for the breathing apparatus. The 'breathing exercises' on the other hand aim at the method of breathing, at quality not quantity; their principle, as for all formative exercises (see glossary) to which systematically they belong, is to improve co-ordination.

The expression 'lung exercises' is rejected by the Viennese physiologist Durig; he has drawn attention to the fact that the lungs cannot be exercised since they are not active in breathing. The phrase is used here as the correct expression, 'exercises of the breathing apparatus', would be much too clumsy.

Without sufficient exercise of his lungs nobody can have good breathing. Breathing exercises, which are used only to teach correct co-ordination, cannot take the place of vigorous exercise. The reason for the exercise is not important, a person's work or his leisure time activities such as swimming, playing games or gardening, may force him to heightened breathing.

However, one must not think that the breathing exercises are superfluous. It cannot be taken for granted that a person will breathe correctly when he is at rest, let alone when he is moving. Like every movement, the movement which brings about the change of air in the lungs can be carried out in different ways. Breathing is, it is true, like other vital processes, automatic; but unlike, for example, the activity of the heart, the movement of breathing can, because it is brought about by striated (skeletal) muscles, also arise voluntarily and consciously and in this freedom lies the possibility of error. Through breathing exercises one learns to breathe correctly; the muscular play which dilates the thorax and thus brings about the inflow of air can be influenced by exercises. How this must be carried out in individual cases (age, proficiency, etc.,) will not concern us here.

In order to understand the possibilities for improvement one must first know the forces that bring about the movement of breathing. A breath consists of inhalation and exhalation. Inhalation is physiologically the active phase; it is brought about by muscular power. Exhalation is physiologically passive; it is a result of gravity against which the thorax is lifted, of elastic forces (costal cartilage) which are brought into play by the inhalation, of the tension in the lungs—supplemented when necessary by muscular power. Psychologically it is the other way round; whilst breathing in one must remain passive, waiting, whilst in breathing out one can shape the current of air by speaking or singing.

It is necessary to mention too that the inspiratory muscles have great superiority over the expiratory muscles, and this easily leads to the inhalation predominating and the exhalation becoming insufficient as soon as stronger demands are made on the breathing apparatus. It must be remembered that breathing is a process incredibly easily disturbed; it is influenced by all physical and mental occurrences. The fact that some other person is watching the breathing is enough to change it!

From this fact, and many others not mentioned here, follow all sorts of important things for training correct breathing: making the breath sound encourages excellent control over exhalation; it would be an advantage to their health if people

were to sing more! Hofbauer (1921) makes his pupils hum, this
is an exercise which can always be used and is always useful.
Turning one's attention to inhalation, one has to learn to wait
for the inhalation, to allow the air to flow in, instead of drawing
it in as is usual. Muscular tension must never become visible,
especially not in the face or neck; the breathing must always be
as light as a feather without violence or groaning and snorting.
The breath comes and goes gently and lightly, invisibly and
inaudibly.

The importance of breathing through the nose cannot be
emphasized too much. Of course there are situations when one
cannot make do with breathing through the nose alone: anyone
running for his life is entitled to open his mouth. However, these
are exceptional situations which just have to be lived through
and which may result in worse damage than mouth breathing,
for example, injury or shock. Normally one must breathe both
in and out through the nose. This must be particularly emphasized; inhalation through the nose will be accepted by everyone
in order to clean, warm and moisten the air, but many are
dubious about exhalation. Nobody can, over a period of time,
open and close the mouth twice in every breath; besides this,
too much moisture is extracted from the mucous membranes by
breathing out through the mouth.

With practice one can learn to push the limits between nose
and mouth breathing further and further. And each step represents a gain. Mountain-climbing, running, etc., must be so
carried through that one can make do with breathing through
one's nose—this is just a question of timing. And it is better to
arrive at the top of a mountain somewhat later but breathing
calmly than earlier but exhausted and gasping.

Breathing exercises. Through breathing exercises one learns
to breathe correctly. This sentence needs some explanation.
What is breathing correctly? Can a process which happens all
the time, nearly always subconsciously, occur incorrectly? The
sentence from Kleist (1810), 'What havoc consciousness can
wreak in human movement' might lead one to suppose that
breathing would be more likely to become incorrect if one were
paying attention to it. And since in breathing exercises one does
pay attention to the breathing it might be possible to do more
harm than good. The fact too that a number of very serious

'modern gymnastic systems' (see glossary, *Gymnastik*) which originally studied breathing in some detail later rejected all direct intervention in the breathing process could be interpreted in this way. However, certain observations are opposed to this view and give one something to think about: by influencing breathing it is possible to help people who have various problems such as nervous disorders or insomnia and this possibility is increasingly being exploited by doctors. Yet this is only successful with a certain type of breathing: the breathing described as *typus inversus* is of no help, indeed proves actually to be one of the causes of such nervous disturbances.

Even if in general, breathing is carried on correctly as long as it is left to the care of the unconscious, nevertheless, it can change to incorrect breathing and this can become permanent. How is it possible to safeguard against this?

One sure way is to live as healthy and natural a life as possible with simple, unspiced food, loose clothing, suitable variation between work and recreation, enough exercise if one's profession does not entail physical work, and other such things. Yet since everyone cannot be sure of achieving all this, and since there are also other reasons for incorrect breathing, proceeding from inside one, this is not enough. Every person has to learn how breathing proceeds naturally, and must be brought to understand that correct breathing is of much more importance for physical and mental health than is usually thought, and that breathing must proceed correctly both at rest and in movement. This is what breathing exercises are for, and it follows from this that they are useful and necessary even for those who breathe correctly. Of course their usefulness depends on their being carried out in the right way, at a suitable time, and in conjunction with all the other exercises which serve to educate man physically.

The work of the physical educator should therefore be aimed at making everyone breathe correctly and know what correct breathing is like and how to preserve it.

Among the various questions which result from this discussion of breathing exercises that of the type of breathing seems to be in most urgent need of clarification. By this is meant the way in which the muscles, which bring about breathing, work together. This can happen in very different ways—luckily for us—for because of this we can breathe in all possible positions and

postures and under the different demands made on us. We will
not go into the question of whether and how all these circumstances influence the type of breathing. For the time being we
will discuss here only breathing whilst at rest.

The question of the type of breathing can best be clarified if
one introduces the technical term 'the initial stage of a movement'. This means the region in which a movement is first
visible, the place where it begins. This is something which can
be seen and this removes the discussion from the realm of specu-
lation and draws it into the field of precise observation. And this
is important; when we want to clarify questions of form we must
stick to what we can see with our eyes. The diaphragm and its
action cannot be seen, we can see only the effects of its contraction and relaxation. One must therefore observe the trunk and
determine by observation how the breathing works in and on it.
First the abdominal wall is seen to bulge outwards a little, and
immediately afterwards the thorax dilates. This happens with
every breath, even the smallest, all at the same time, in less than
a second, not in sequence or in separate sections as unfortunately
it has to be described. So whether the visible effects are smaller
or greater in a breath is not important; the initial stage of the
movement is the same whether it goes on to be high and steep
or occurs flatly and gently.

In the manner of breathing known as *typus inversus* the initial
stage is different: the inhalation begins with the abdominal wall
being drawn in, and on exhalation it dilates. This inverted movement of the abdominal wall is the real characteristic of inverted
breathing, whether the frequency and amplitude of the movements of breathing are large or small. Hofbauer, who has made
a special study of breathing (1921), confirms that: 'Nature
knows only one type of breathing . . . the only difference
which can be made lies in the size of the dilation'.

This shows that the technical term 'initial stage of a movement' is well suited to producing complete clarity. If one says,
for example, that men tend to breathe from the abdomen and
women from the costal region, one does not know exactly
whether a difference of degree is meant by this (perhaps in the
sense 'the movement in the abdominal region, after the same
initial stage, is more clearly stamped in the man than in the
woman') or one of type ('the breathing movement proceeds,

independently of the amount of effort, in a quite different way in the woman, that is in the sense of *typus inversus*').

On this one could also remark that in one and the same man the movements of breathing are more or less clearly visible at different places according to the position of his body. The view found in most of the older textbooks of anatomy and physiology, that there is a difference in breathing according to sex, is no longer upheld by later authors such as Braus (1921). The present author has observed the breathing of women of various ages for many years and has scarcely ever seen the breathing supposed to be typically feminine. In every case, as long as they were at rest, inhalation began with slight dilation of the abdominal wall.

There is a way of achieving an 'incorrect' initial stage fairly easily and surely: the command to breathe deeply leads many people to do it at once. Mechanical means too, like lacing the body in with a strong belt, bring about incorrect breathing, a change which lasts for a time after removing the belt and then recedes again. In this way people have been able to bring about artificially in men the supposedly typically feminine way of breathing. This consideration makes it seem likely that the 'feminine' breathing of the older textbooks is, at least in part, a result of the tight bodices worn by generations of women.

All these questions should be tested out on a large number of people; the results would have to be recorded by objective means such as photography, films and X-rays. Measurements could be quoted in support of these but they alone can never serve to clarify questions of form.

Now to return to the question of breathing exercises: they are not there to influence the frequency and amplitude of the breathing movements for the muscles governing breathing are regulated by an autonomous impulse-forming organ which adapts its force to the conditions reigning at any given moment. One must not interfere arbitrarily with this regulation provided by the respiratory centre. So any command to breathe more quickly or slowly, more shallowly or deeply, is incorrect. Especially dangerous is the command, unfortunately still common, to inhale deeply. The inspiratory muscles are much stronger than the expiratory ones; this is the reason why one can so easily overdo it.

Breathing exercises can and should assure the correct initial stage of breathing and its correct course. One must learn to allow the inhalation 'to happen' instead of, as is usual, drawing in the air. That breathing to numbers is most unsuitable for this is obvious; it is equally obvious that such exercises demand calmness and composure and fit in badly among exercises directed at ambition, records, exhibition—external success. One ought to bring people out of our noisy modern life, with its tendency to lump people together, into stillness, and this is not easy but it is worth while if it succeeds. The secret of 'natural' inhalation is that one does nothing towards it, but just experiences how something happens when one's own will plays no part in it on pain of making everything go wrong. 'Natural' inhalation belongs to the natural part of us; if we have lost it we can regain it only by making our over-active will rest, and allowing nature to take command.

One can only agree with the Rotenburger Schule (see glossary, *Gymnastik*): 'No breathing exercises should be done before the inhalation impulse has consciously been set to rights. Breathing gymnastics are disastrous'. For this reason the popular linking of inhalation with movements is to be rejected; this disturbs the feeling of passivity and leads one away from what is really important. Systematically one ought to range this 'practising' of natural inhalation with the breathing exercises, for like breathing exercises it aims at improving the co-ordination of the muscles concerned. One can also 'practise' singing absolutely on pitch—there too the innervation improves indirectly by careful listening to the notes produced, not by paying attention to the muscles concerned.

Beside the question of the type of breathing, the rhythm of the breathing (the sequence in time of the movements of breathing) is also of interest. The best image of this is the wave. The movements of breathing always have this character, whether the peaks of the waves follow one another quickly or slowly, or whether they are high or low. Although, as already mentioned, one must not influence this deliberately, here too there is possibility of and necessity for practice. This lies at the change-over from the crest of the wave to its valley and vice versa. Usually two phases of breathing are given: inhalation and exhalation. The Hade Kallmeyer gymnastic system (see glossary, *Gymnastik*), described under the title 'Rhythmic Breathing', makes its pupils practise in four stages in a rhythm 4:2:4:2, inhalation and exhalation equally long and the pauses in between half as long. The triple breathing rhythm called for by the Rotenburger Schule (see glossary, *Gymnastik*) with a pause before each new inhalation seems preferable to me: it is a natural result of waiting for the inhalation impulse, whilst a pause at the height of the inhalation brings with it the danger of stress.

Because of the predominance of the inspiratory muscles the rule is that one should continually remind whoever is exercising to breathe out sufficiently: for this the humming exercises suggested by Hofbauer (1921) and their conjunction with a certain number of steps whilst, for example, climbing a mountain are very useful. Then one need not worry about sufficient inhalation; the thorough exhalation leads to this of its own accord.

A further question of interest to teachers of physical education is that of the linking together of breathing and movement. In progressive movements like running, swimming, rowing, etc., the pupil should fit the movement in with his breathing, not the other way round. In movements which demand an expenditure of strength once, at the beginning, like lifting, etc., the expenditure of strength belongs to the phase of exhalation and should not be connected with a cramped holding of the breath at the height of the inhalation.

Thorough training of correct breathing is unthinkable without speaking and singing. 'Our goal', say the Rotenburgs, 'is natural inhalation and exhalation suitable for artistic purposes'. And they continue: 'Only with exhalation can one deal voluntarily, and this can be done only in conjunction with the voice'. These two sentences contain in brief what the physical education teacher has to do: with the help of all the other teachers, he lays a foundation on which the English teacher and the singing teacher build. In physical exercises the teacher has far less opportunity than usual of hearing his pupils speak, so he can scarcely work on exhalation for artistic purposes. The care of breathing, one of the most important and complicated tasks, thus does not fall on the physical education teacher alone; he cannot complete it by himself. What an important difference it would make if all teachers were conscious of their common responsibility, and strove with all their might for clarity and unity!

In conclusion, all these simple, clear rules for the training of correct breathing can be summarized: becoming accustomed to fresh air and generous airing of rooms, to loose clothing, much singing, enough lung exercise, breathing through the nose, becoming accustomed to thorough exhalation (humming exercises), learning correct beginning of inhalation and correct course followed by each breath, waiting for inhalation, never drawing in air arbitrarily, breathing without violence or visible tension, doing hard work during exhalation, not 'straining'. These rules are not mysterious; they can be observed always and everywhere, and they assure effective and yet sufficiently careful handling of the process of breathing so vital to life.

Generally speaking people's feet are in a bad way. Doctors' statistics prove that much of their work is concerned with deformities and complaints of the foot. The Swedish orthopaedist Haglund (1923) indicates that more than half of his patients come to him on account of their feet. And anyone can look about him and see the same thing: feet in general are a weak point.

Evolutionarily the foot is a recent formation. Standing and walking upright are peculiar to man, who appears relatively late in the history of the earth. Millions of years of organic life lie behind him. His statics are continually in danger. If man does not make an effort to remain upright he succumbs to gravity.

The foot is connected to the lower part of the leg by upper and lower joints (talo-tibial and talo-calcaneo-navicular joints) and can be moved in practically any direction. In addition the whole bone structure of the foot can be moved on its own. The skeleton of the foot consists of twenty-six little bones connected to one another by means of not very flexible joints, thus they can move a little in relation to one another. Because of this the foot can always fit itself snugly to the ground, whether it slopes or is uneven, so long as stiffness (or rigidity) of the bone structure does not prevent this. On the other hand the stability of the foot is affected by its flexibility, especially when carrying a weight and when standing still.

The correct relative positioning of the twenty-six little bones is assured by the muscles; the ligaments also play a part but the play of the muscles is decisive. When walking, running and jumping on natural, unpaved ground the demands made on the muscles change continually, so they can easily do this work, but static demands are different. Everyone knows from experience how much more exhausting standing is than walking for the same length of time. If static demands are made on the foot repeatedly for long periods, the muscles gradually fail, they become 'insufficient' and then the foot degenerates rapidly.

A healthy foot with strong, well-developed muscles, on which not too many static demands are made, is quite able to carry the weight of the body but if the loading lasts too long (as in standing professions) the muscles no longer support the arch, the foot collapses, and serious, irremedial flat-footedness may result. Defects can also come into being if there is a great increase of weight, for example, in pregnancy. In the same way a constitutional lack of muscle tone or a weakness of the connective tissue can cause lowered functional capacity of the foot.

In addition to all this the feet are usually badly treated. The European clothes them in shoes and stockings; this means that for two thirds of their life the feet are in coverings impenetrable by light and air. The skin of the feet is insufficiently aired, and is often continuously damp and shut in from the light. Frequently too the coverings are badly shaped. Stockings do not correspond at all to the shape of an undeformed foot. This is not as unimportant as many people would like to think; it has been proved by means of X-rays that the pull of a silk stocking is enough to deflect the toes from their proper position. Our great-grandchildren will probably one day laugh as heartily about the people who pull symmetrical stockings over their asymmetrical feet as our children laugh about the symmetrical shape generally to be found in cheap shoes of a generation ago.

Most shoes are not much better suited to the shape of the foot. Nowadays it is usual for walking shoes to have low heels but many of them have bad inside edges and often they do not allow the toes enough play. Most people do not believe this, simply because they have no clear picture of an undeformed human foot: one where there are no edges on the toes, no callosities and corns and no nails pushed sideways! One has to observe for a long time the feet of little children and people who always go barefoot to accustom one's eyes to the fact that there are no pointed feet, only pointed shoes.

The incorrect shape of the foot-coverings has two harmful results: mechanically it stops the toes moving, presses them together and impedes their movement; and it gives the toes a different position from the natural one. From the point of view of the mid-line of the body the big toes are forced outwards and the others inwards, so that the fan-like form of the foot gradually disappears. The great importance of the toes can be judged from the fact that losing the toes is reckoned as a forty per cent disability, nearly as much as losing the whole foot, which is evaluated as a forty to fifty per cent disability.

The disastrous thing about foot deformities is that, once they have begun, they get worse and worse; they never return to the norm of their own accord. This is easily understood if one imagines that something which bears weight, such as the leg of a chair, is cracked, under pressure the crack will get worse and worse and the affair can end only in catastrophe. The one possible remedy is to splint the leg of the chair, in other words to force it into its original position and fix it mechanically.

This comparison shows the basic facts. Another image reproduces the special conditions in the foot better. Imagine a three-legged stool. One leg corresponds to the *os calcis*, and so points backwards. The second slants forwards and outwards and corresponds to the fifth or little toe. The third points straight forwards and corresponds to the big toe. This stool is not well built mechanically, it is long and narrow and the three legs are on the short sides. A stool constructed like this will easily tip over sideways. In the human foot this tipping will occur more easily on one side than on the other because the heel bone naturally slants outwards a little, so the foot very easily tips over inwards.

Only a strong big toe can prevent this happening. In the stool which we have used as a comparison the danger of tipping over becomes less in proportion as the two legs pointing forwards diverge outwards. So the more the big and little toes are pushed together by stockings and shoes the worse this is for the position of the foot. From this example one can see how invaluable is the play of the toes for preserving the correct position and form of the foot.

What then must we do to assure healthy foot development for ourselves and above all for our children?

Before everything else children must go barefoot a lot, especially on natural, unpaved ground. One should always make use of excursions to let them walk, for a while at least, barefoot in forest or meadow.

The giant Antaios drew his strength from touching the earth; our feet attain their full strength and flexibility only by touching the ground when walking, running and jumping. This contact applies countless stimuli to the muscles of the feet which could never be replaced by invented exercises. All these stimuli are eliminated if the hard and rigid sole of a shoe is between the foot and the ground.

At home soft shoes ought to be worn far more than is usual (this would also help to keep our dwellings clean). The fear that soft shoes cause flat feet is ungrounded. This would be a hazard only if one were to stand in them for a long time.

Standing should be avoided as much as possible. Housework which does not definitely have to be done standing should be carried out sitting. Anyone whose job causes him to stand a lot should not sit but lie down in his free time, because the circulation of the blood to the legs is facilitated by the horizontal position. In such periods of rest too, even if they are only short, it is worth the effort to take one's shoes off. It is highly beneficial to be able to move one's toes freely and for the feet to get air and if possible light; and this benefit could be had so cheaply!

Our stockings must be refashioned. Really the industry should be forced by the buyers to make asymmetrical stockings; only a short time ago in a textile paper there was a suggestion for the reform of stockings—so perhaps one day the industry will force the buyers to take healthy stockings. And shoes! They should have straight inside edges since they are otherwise bound to push the big toe out of position. Nearly all shoes made today lack room for the individually varying position of the big toe and by wearing such shoes a person treads his big toe more and more into a kink outwards and an inwards list. Chilblains, etc., are the direct result of this deformity occasioned solely by badly constructed shoes. So the inside edges of our shoes need to be radically reshaped. Instead of, as is usual, forming an open-ended angle with one another at the toe, they should be straight. Only then would they allow the big toes to keep their natural position instead of pushing them into the other toes. Once this development has begun—and a small angle in relation to the axis of the foot is enough for this—it goes further and further and eventually leads to *hallux valgus* with all its evil consequences.

So what each individual must and can do to keep his feet healthy is, briefly, as follows: avoid unnecessary standing, rest lying down instead of sitting, reduce the time spent wearing shoes to the minimum, only wear shoes with hard soles when necessary, walk a lot barefoot on natural ground, wear stockings and shoes which correspond to the form of the foot.

Besides this, what can be achieved by special foot exercises? Three things: the foot muscles must be strengthened, the feeling for the mobility of the toes must be regained, and the right foot-work must be learnt and practised.

Strengthening the muscles cannot be achieved without weighting the feet, for the foot muscles are used to working under the weight of the body; if one removes the weight the movements may be successful in awakening a feeling for the play of the toes, which is usually completely lost in the shoes, but the muscles are not strengthened. Only walking, running and jumping, if possible on natural ground and barefoot, and mounting and climbing, apply the stimuli which give the foot muscles their strength.

> To regain a feeling for the mobility of the foot, especially the toes, all exercises are effective which correspond to grasping—that is making a fist; grasping and picking up an object (acorns, little pieces of wood); screwing up a cloth, etc.

Such exercises can and should be done daily by children as a game, and the adult too will feel their beneficial influence if he includes them amongst his morning exercises.

> For learning correct footwork we can give only a few general pieces of advice; when walking, running and jumping, exaggerate the spread of the toes and the grasping movement (imagine the toes are clutching the ground); when setting the foot down, consciously spread out the big toes; when walking along the narrow side of a form, or the horizontal bar, or when climbing up the rungs of a ladder, set the foot down on the ball and 'hold on to' the support; when standing, spread the toes wide and 'clutch' the ground hard.

All finer details of treatment, especially when it is a question of important deviations which have led to complaints or even deformities, must be left to the teachers trained in remedial work, and in cases of disease to the doctor.

Section III

The role of physical education in general education

There are fields of work in which the necessity for independently constructed theory is universally recognized. Behind the highly developed technology which so strongly determines the face of our age stands research of a purely scientific nature in the fields of chemistry, physics, etc. Even when this research does not stem from practical considerations but is solely directed at increasing our knowledge, everyone knows that it will eventually benefit practical work.

It is different in the field of educational work. Here, where the unique nature of the personal element makes it very difficult to discover general rules, the opinion easily develops that theory is unnecessary, indeed even harmful, because it dims the eye for what is peculiar to each new 'case' and thus destroys the impartiality of the treatment. From this the conclusion is drawn that theory in general is superfluous in this field of work.

This opinion often governs one part of pedagogy, physical education. It is necessary to examine more closely whether this is justified.

We will begin with a brief general reflection. Man stands in life chiefly as a doer not a thinker; he has to come to terms with the world that surrounds him, and endeavours to assert himself in it. The Greek word θεωρειν shows well how 'action' is changed into 'theory', for the word means to look at, consider, ponder on. Man thinks about his actions and so goes beyond the present in space and time. Pestalozzi expresses this in the words: 'Man paves the way to his goal with the flame of thought'. This development is of decisive importance, and cannot be reversed.

As long as thought is tied to action there is no problem; this only begins when facts and associations which go beyond what is necessary for mere action are investigated, when one begins, so to speak, to think of storing knowledge. Theory in the strict and real sense begins when knowledge is sought for its own sake.

A treasure-house of knowledge results which goes far beyond the life of each individual. Many people, often widely separated by time and space, take part in mastering a field of work scientifically. Using medicine as an example will help to make this clear. Medicine means the art of restoring and preserving health, the art of healing; so the real upholder of the work is the practising doctor. With him is associated the research worker, who often has nothing to do with sick people but perhaps raises bacteria cultures in his laboratory in order to investigate what conditions their life. The doctor inspired by the desire to help and the research worker with his urge for knowledge belong together; both serve medicine, which is at once a science and an art. The practice of healing has always existed—and still does today—where people help themselves by means of remedies learnt by experience and handed down by tradition. However, no one would say that working on medicine in a purely scientific and theoretical way does it any harm.

In the field of physical education too there is a practice based on experience and tradition; but no one should doubt the need for theoretical clarification. The literature on gymnastics, usually aimed at aiding teaching, has neglected scientific clarity and precision of concepts. This has given science proper a mistrust of this literature which is not entirely unjustified. Besides the general mistrust of theory we must also overcome the special mistrust of 'the science of gymnastics'. Yet mutual give and take, fruitful exchanges between neighbouring scientific fields, cannot become reality until the obvious and eternal principles of science (like clarity of thought and conceptual precision, careful exploitation of previous research, bibliography, etc.) are generally recognized and carried through as far as the actual treatment of questions in physical education.

There are difficulties in amalgamating scientific work on physical education with the training of teachers. When students, who are very able in the physical work, have difficulties with the theory, some people still say: 'why should they have to learn so much—as long as they are good at gymnastics'! And so all scientific work in this field is put in question.

These two questions, theory in the field of physical education, and the training of teachers, must be kept well apart.

To understand the first question clearly one only needs to go back to the comparison with medicine. Medicine has a wide scientific basis which cannot be investigated too thoroughly.

Besides this, medicine always worries more about the intellectual side because doctors know that one cannot heal a sick man simply by treating his body; the doctor has to know and take into account his patient's psychological identity and social position. So medicine, as a science, must also be based on the science of the mind—a very large area of knowledge to investigate.

This is even more true of education. If 'writing about education means writing about nearly everything', investigating it means investigating nearly everything, at least everything which concerns man. This is true of physical education too; it is a large subject posing special independent questions. Here, as in other fields of knowledge, it is to be expected that the results of theoretical research would flow into and fertilize the practice of physical education.

Concerning the second question, that of the training of teachers, if physical education is given over solely to practice and consciously or unconsciously suppresses theory it is cut off from further development; it remains fixed in its traditional habits. An old peasant from the mountains could not be reproached with the fact that he had not got beyond household remedies but what would one say of a doctor who, in the age of asepsis, tried to treat a wound with spiders' webs? Similarly, what should one say to a physical education teacher who tried to educate children in correct breathing and good posture in the unbiological, military way which was for years applied in all good faith? Then no one knew better, but today there is no excuse for using these methods.

It is of real concern to everyone that the technical training given fully corresponds with the modern state of knowledge. Ordinary people are gradually adopting hygienic methods in their daily lives through the influence of the doctors. Teaching in all subjects must also be continually changing in order to adopt the broadened and deepened knowledge of today, and it is obvious that teachers, who are and can be specialists in their subjects, should be given the highest technical training.

So an affirmative answer is to be given to both questions— the first of the justification for, and uses of, theoretical work in the problems of physical education, and the second of the necessity for using all available knowledge of the theory and practice of the subject in training teachers. This is not to say that every teacher who has to give a few lessons somewhere in physical exercise should be thus trained; and one should not think that a theoretical training alone can assure educationally and technically good teaching.

One is not guilty of intellectualism in demanding a scientific way of working in the field of physical education, but one is at fault if one denies theory *per se* because one knows individual teachers who teach well without thorough, correct theory.

The nucleus of all the changes that have occurred over the past years is the turning away from the material as the central core of the work to the needs of the individual child. The question of how to get the pupil to learn the prescribed exercises quickly and surely and reach the goal of the class is no longer asked, but—how does one further the pupil's development? So it is the child, not the material, that determines the work.

At once the requirement which is now at the heart of all reform in education and teaching is recognized. Exercising and unfolding the children's powers takes the place of imparting knowledge to them. This means much to physical education for it suffered greatly from the idea that only learning was important. In academic subjects the material itself is important. There is more to reading and writing, arithmetic, geography, and foreign languages than learning. The child has to master the content in order to find his way about in the world, whereas in physical education the material by itself is of little consequence. Only in certain branches of the subject, as for example swimming or skiing, is there any real usefulness; but generally the exercises themselves have very little practical meaning. Gymnastics, conceived as an 'object of learning', had become an inferior subject for the material it had to impart was less important than that of the other subjects taught in school. The conception of gymnastics as an aid to development is a real turning point. Now it fits into general education in a quite different manner.

It must not be thought that the relative unimportance of the material means that it does not matter what the pupils do; if that were the case one could just as well stick to the old state of affairs. We do know rather more about physical exercise now than we used to; we also know more about the way children develop, physically and intellectually. From the value of the exercises and need for them (which is more than a physical need) a biologically determined choice of material arises. Selecting the exercise material on biological grounds is a very different process from accepting and using traditional activities that can be understood only in their historical setting. This latter method of selection certainly cannot be justified today.

The moment one no longer considers the exercises as a goal in themselves but as an educational means, thus subjecting them to pedagogical criticism, one begins to think them out quite differently. Long before a nation begins to work consciously on the physical education of its offspring, physical exercises are present as a voluntary activity, as games, dances and sports. Teachers find many forms already in existence, and have the task of sifting through them to discover their educational value. Not all existing exercises have educational value, just as not all existing literature has educational value. We have, for example, ballet technique and its set of exercises: an age which adopts everything and is actually proud of doing everything will happily adopt the ballet technique and carefully develop means by which the children will be able to learn it quickly and surely. Whereas, if there is a demand for pedagogic physical education, the question will first have to be answered whether the technique helps the pupil to develop. Only when it has been decided that it does, can one begin to think of the means for acquiring this technique. To consider another example—the game of football: one point of view is that football is *the* sport nowadays, so it must be cultivated in the schools; the other that football leads to roughness and should under no circumstances be accepted in the schools. Teachers, however, consider whether the game is of value physically and intellectually and at what age it is of benefit to the pupils. That the game is often played as a business nowadays says nothing against the game itself. Again, can gymnastic tricks on apparatus be of definite help to the pupil at any stage of his development? Should they be used on their own or along with other exercises?

The choice has to be based on the pupil's need for exercise. It must not be arbitrary, but biologically well-founded. The child goes through the same stages of physical development as humanity in general has gone through, so for his education the biologically old movement forms like running, jumping, climbing, throwing, etc., are more necessary than the biologically recent art forms of vaulting and agility exercises on apparatus, which were for a long time thought to be the most important part of gymnastics. The systems which introduced exercises consisting of single movements, which had been broken up and arbitrarily put together again, instead of the basic and essential activities without which man would never have been able to assert himself in the world, are today seen to be biologically insufficient. Life no longer enforces physical effort, so physical education must do so, especially for growing children; they must repeat, in shortened form, the development of the race.

When the physical activities of the people were performed only for enjoyment and recreation, the schools could simply take them over and in so doing, take over a piece of life, but as these became more of a business, thereby losing the dignity of every-day life (a development which has been proceeding extraordinarily quickly in recent years), it became necessary for the schools to fashion their own approach to physical activities. They could no longer follow adult practice, which is not governed by pedagogical considerations and grows according to different rules. This development is, of course, an expression of the nature of modern man in its extravagance, affectation and delight in the spectacular but it should not be used in schools. This distinction, and we have to thank Gaulhofer (Gaulhofer and Streicher, 1930) for its clarity, is what actually leads to the development of physical activities as an educational pursuit. Here only the pedagogical point of view is valid, as in the rest of the work done in education, but one has to struggle all the time to maintain this standpoint. It is always in jeopardy. Again and again evaluations and opinions from other spheres are allowed to enter, which may be justifiable in themselves but have nothing to do with education. The teacher must pursue the pedagogic viewpoint relentlessly otherwise he is not acting as an educator but, at best, as a trainer. The essential difference between the leisure time activity of adults and the physical education of young people is certainly not yet clear to everyone. Consider the image of the good gymnast which for years made people force children into a scheme of movement foreign to them and harmful, or of the athlete who sacrifices everything, even his health, to set up a new record. Think of the acrobatic flexibility which nowadays many people think a dancer should have, no matter what means are used to obtain it. All these value judgements are foreign to education, and true physical education must be freed of them as quickly and thoroughly as possible.

This does not mean that, for example, no achievement can be called for in physical education but achievement is a means not a goal. A certain level must be attained because otherwise no growth stimulus can be exerted, but there is a limit beyond which one cannot go if one is to have biologically good results; how the sporting world, with its interest in world records, judges this level of achievement is of no importance. The ambition of individual teachers who cannot bear such criticisms and so over-tax the strength of their pupils must be frustrated. This danger is probably greater for boys, with whom it may be easier to overstep the limit set by the educational context, than for girls. In girls' physical education, on the other hand, achievement is sometimes rated too low because the girls are being judged by the physical neglect which has been the lot of women for centuries, so that no result at all is obtained.

However, extremes of athletic accomplishment are not the only danger today. There is also danger in the unusual, exciting or startling. One must be aware how films, stage shows, etc., seem to be trying to extend the limits of what man can do. The exaggerated flexibility which may be seen in girls' gymnastics has one of its roots in the type of dancing seen in variety and revue. No one bothers to consider whether this flexibility has any value. A certain way of bearing oneself and moving is modern, the 'slim line'. That physical exercises can help to achieve this is not disputed, and some people are able to see physical exercises for women and girls only from this point of view. This attitude colours their judgement but naturally has nothing whatsoever to do with education.

The unconditional governing of the work by educational principles brings with it the benefits of objectivity. To find the best educational framework all the facts which science gathers about the physical and intellectual effect of exercise and the development of young people must be taken into account without prejudice. Physical education is no longer dependent on the opinions of the day.

For the development of the work for girls in particular this objectivity is something of a release. Now, at last, they are free of the uneducational forces which have restricted them for years. For a long time callisthenics, that is education in beauty and grace, ruled unopposed. Although we cannot now bear the old forms because our conception of beauty has changed, callisthenics still hold sway, to a great extent, in people's minds. In some places, on the other hand, there has been a deplorable attempt to make women more masculine and an exaggerated desire for high sporting achievement appeared. For years girls' physical education was tossed between these two pitfalls and never came to peaceful, objective development. Only a clear decision for purely pedagogic principles can give a solution.

Yet for this not only the physical side is necessary but the intellectual too. Whilst the material was of central importance it provided something physical which could be understood as such—one was not forced to think of the intellectual side. Even if there was here and there an allusion to something intellectual like obedience, co-operation, orderliness, the teacher could easily come to the conclusion that he had done his duty if the children had learnt the prescribed exercise. Whereas, if one poses the question: has the child's development been furthered, one inevitably comes upon the intellectual element because this is part of the child. A child is never something purely physical; the intellectual side is always present and cannot be eliminated whether he is reckoning, or drawing, or doing gymnastics. Conversely he is not something purely intellectual, as some people would like to make one think, either; the physical side is very real. One can say that the child, like humanity in general, is conditioned but not determined by the physical element. We must cultivate and develop him physically if he is to become a complete person, but we cannot and must not ignore the intellectual aspect. In other words, from time to time in education the intellectual side has been rated too highly and the biological basis has been forgotten. Nowadays we know that the health of a nation is destroyed by a purely intellectual attitude. Physical exercise rises daily in general estimation but it would be a great mistake to rate the physical side too highly and think that physical exercise alone was enough. It is not just a question of doing gymnastics but of how one does them. Not every kind of exercising furthers education to full humanity. Unless it aims intellectually at the same goal as the rest of education, physical exercise does not add anything to education. As in intellectual training one must do nothing to harm the body, so in physical education one must do nothing to harm the intellect. Only then can one speak of harmonious education.

This deep conviction of the unity of man runs through the new physical education modifying many of its details. One can and must anchor the intellectual element in it, if it is to serve education. Physical exercise which only comprehends the body is not even right for the body, not to mention the whole person. Once this conviction has clearly and visibly begun to determine physical exercise, the opposition of those who think that such exercise alienates one from the intellectual life and that it is impossible to unite physical and intellectual education will disappear; they think that one has to opt for one or the other, and decide for the intellectual side, renouncing the physical. The conviction that it is 'not an intellect, not a body, but a person that one is educating' is once again alive today, and gives modern physical education its special stamp.

The inclusion of the intellectual aspect in work on physical education is clearly mirrored in the training of teachers of physical education. Whilst this was formerly limited to anatomy, physiology, etc., it now includes such subjects as psychology, growth and development, sociology, etc. Let us also add here that in modern literature on physical education the intellectual connections are worked out much more definitely than they used to be, just as on the other side the physical aspect plays a far greater role in discussion on intellectual matters. A knowledge of the unity of body and intellect is not, of course, new. Anyone who, filled by the burning question of the possibility of intellectualized exercise, immerses himself in Schiller's philosophical writings (1794) or reads Kleist's *Marionette Theatre* (1810) will find confirmation upon confirmation of the fact that the question of education cannot be considered from a purely intellectual standpoint, nor can it be considered from a purely physical one. The special character of man rests in his sensual and ethical nature, and the question of education cannot be solved by neglecting or overrating one side or the other. Physical education must stay built into education as a whole, otherwise it goes wholly astray.

17 *Expression and representation*

The preservation of the capacity for expression and representation is one of the goals of physical education, and a movement can be expressive only if it is stamped by the individuality of its exponent. In practical terms this is a question of allowing the peculiarities of the individual to grow as freely and abundantly as is consistent with his fitting into the whole. One can train a child to a certain way of moving just as one can train a tree to grow in a certain form, like a bottle or a cock, by clipping it. To a former age this seemed the essence of the art of gardening. Today we find a tree more beautiful in its natural form, delicately divided yet remaining unified, rather than artificially lopped. No wonder if in gymnastics too we prefer free, personal, individual movement to the drill form.

It is of great importance to education whether one decides for the drill form or for the natural form of movement, for basically life has no other means of expression than through movement. All forms and images, drawing and painting, writing, speech, music, all these are in the final resort movement in which life expresses itself. Thus in a person's peculiarities of movement we foster or destroy the roots of all individual expression of life. So the department which attempts to influence education by means of movement alone, for which movement is the material for training the child, can have a decisive influence on the development of his whole capacity for expression. It can hinder or help the efforts of other departments to attain this capacity for expression.

To get a clear idea of the possibilities open to physical education it is first of all necessary to ascertain the meaning of the much used but unfortunately ambiguous terms expression and representation—without this, clarification is impossible.

The present analysis is based on the work of Ludwig Klages. The terms expression and representation are here used only in the sense adopted by him.

(a) *Expression*
First some sentences from Klages' *Expressive Movement and the Power of Figuration* (1921):

The usual division of living movements into voluntary and involuntary ones is to blame for the fact that one speaks of the former in the same way as one does of the latter, yet only those which occur involuntarily occur of their own accord.

As a ship moves with or without steering but not without some mechanism so every living movement needs some propulsive force and this is always involuntary, even if the rudder of the will unites with it in those movements which for want of a better term we call voluntary. So every action shows traits of expression.

Whilst the will has complete freedom to choose the means of attaining a goal there is an organic link between psychological activity and the movement by which it is expressed, because of which any change in the one is inevitably followed by a change in the other.

The example in which Klages contrasts the expressive movement with the conscious one makes the matter quite plain. Someone, he says, who has just received a letter the contents of which are extremely annoying, might hit the table with his fist, thus making a movement which could also be made by somebody who was trying to destroy the table. Whereas he is so far from desiring this that he is probably startled by the blow, and will certainly rue it if, for example, a bottle of ink is upset by the blow and its contents spilt on the table. The angry man's blow against the table is an expressive movement. If the recipient of the letter were saddened by its contents he would undoubtedly make some other expressive movement; its form is determined solely by the state of the person who does it—he does not set out to make the movement but feels driven to it; the movement is the result of an inner process which appears intentional to the external world but is actually purposeless. Somebody, on the other hand, who sets out to destroy the table must decide on the means by which to do it, bearing in mind the kind of table that it is; his act must reckon with 'circumstances of this or that nature' otherwise it cannot achieve its goal in the external world. The form of the voluntary movement is therefore determined by the object, but it is not determined by this alone. For 'movements with the same purpose occur in individual ways in different individuals'. The movements with which the man chops up the table (to make further use of our example) would bear his personal stamp; a friend who arrived by chance would be able to recognize him by his movements. 'The term expression, when properly used, denotes those traits in a movement in which psychological activity is manifest. Thus no movement of a living body is quite without expression'. Or more briefly: 'In every voluntary movement the personal form of expression is to be seen'.

In other words one could say: the voluntary movement contains two parts, a practical one dependent on the purpose of the movement and a personal one dependent on the person carrying it out. There are no movements which include only the practical part, the personal element is always present; purely purposeful movements do not occur. There are, however, purely expressive movements, that is, those which contain only the personal element. These always occur unconsciously; one does not intend to do them in advance.

Since the purely expressive movement occurs unconsciously it cannot be influenced by training. A child never has to learn how to give expression to the joy he feels, nor to his fear, embarrassment, expectancy; he is actually much stronger and more fertile at expressing himself than an adult, and education usually teaches him, with varying degrees of success, to repress or at least moderate his expression.

The purely expressive movement is therefore eliminated from the question of training. One cannot do more than give it its due by teaching in a spirit of freedom. It occurs by itself if the psychological urge is there and should not be repressed but allowed to develop.

We therefore have to deal with expression only in voluntary movement. This always bears expressive traits: in reality there is no walking, running or grasping *per se* but only the walking, running or grasping of a particular person at a particular point in time, that is, in a unique combination of inner and outer circumstances.

A movement having a particular purpose can be performed differently by different people, or can even vary when performed by the same person at different times. This fact will be mechanically comprehensible if we take a look at anatomy, which shows that human movements are not obligatory like those of machines but variable: within certain limits, determined by the construction of the joints, there is freedom. One movement from among the many forms which are possible to a person, conforming with the construction and working method of his joints, takes place at a given moment. It appears as a movement picture, speaking to the onlooker not only of the anatomically definable change in the body but also of the being of the person who carries it out, and of his psychological state at the time. Every individual movement picture is a self-contained unit and as such unrepeatable; it appears once and then disappears for ever. In a continuous flow new ones rise up and die away again. What is the same in them, the anatomical occurrence, repeats itself often in the same and other bodies but we never see this in isolation, only as a part of an individual, self-contained, movement picture. Only the latter is real. It is significant that in everyday life the purely physical event, the alteration in the relative position of body and limbs, is looked upon as the essential part only when one is already mentally inclined to observe the movement. Then and only then does one single the movement out from the movement picture. For example, we watch somebody going quickly up to a person— we know immediately whether he is doing it in joy or anger. It is this essential part which we comprehend, and not the steps forward. Or we see a man working; we ascertain what he is doing, whether he is practised in this work or not, whether he is tired or fresh and supple, but never that he bends and stretches his body, raises his arms, etc.

The movement pictures are therefore the only things that matter. In life, movements are always intimately fused with expressive traits and can be separated from them only by careful observation. Movements without expressive traits do not occur; every voluntary movement has, by its very nature, expression.

If expression were determined only from the inside and were completely insulated from external influences, the devitalization of gymnastics would never have occurred and efforts on many sides to win back the capacity for expression would not be necessary. Obviously expression can be impeded, disturbed, indeed even destroyed. Its growth is like that of a plant; under favourable circumstances it develops richly and strongly, under unfavourable ones it atrophies. We can cultivate such development only by trying to get to know better and better the factors determining growth, by listening to nature's own laws and acting according to them.

The question must therefore be raised as to how to frame the work so that expressive movement may develop. It is immediately obvious that no single measure will be of any use but only good general planning.

One must never lose sight of the fact that with expression in voluntary movement too it is a question of making real, inner activity visible, just as it is in purely expressive movement. If one tries to make a movement in such a way that it depicts a definite imagined feeling, one is acting; the term expression should not be used for this. This indeed occurs rather often, and explains the confusion and the many differences of opinion that there are with regard to expression. The difference between expression and representation emerges with extraordinary clarity from a passage in Bode's *Ausdrucksgymnastik* (Expressive Gymnastics, see glossary) : 'to represent definite, orally definable feelings or to teach simple movements for some feeling . . . is the task of an acting academy'. The term 'expressive gymnastics' is therefore not meant to suggest that expressive movements should be practised. It merely describes the aim of regaining the natural, and as such always expressive, manner of moving; the deadening element, which has laid waste our life and therefore also our gymnastics, must be overcome.

Many people think that physical education should not only support but also increase expression, but as soon as one enlists the aid of consciousness one no longer has expression, in the strict sense of the word, but representation. With the help of one's imagination, one can put oneself into a state of joy, pain, surprise, etc., and from this imagined feeling attempt a representation, but all these feelings can only be expressed when one really has them—no thought or practice is needed—they unload themselves in and by means of movement. In common usage the term expression is occasionally used for both expression and representation, but this discussion keeps strictly to the meaning of each word as defined by Klages (1921).

Expression thus describes only those traits which appear in movement without the aid of consciousness. From this follows the fact that one can never influence expression directly but only indirectly. Attempts to influence directly the expressiveness of a movement, to make it 'full of feeling', nearly always lead to affectation and eventually to rubbish.

The well-known aspects of expression will serve to indicate the possibilities open to us for developing the capacity for expression without harming it.

In any kind of work it is necessary, even for the expert, to 'warm up' before the highest capacity for achievement is attained. Similarly, complete fluency of movement is a prerequisite of the fullest expression. In a well-practised games team the expressiveness of the players' movements grows as they 'warm up'. The artist, whether musician, actor, dancer, must 'live' in his role or his piece before he achieves his highest personal measure of expression. The same thing can be seen in orators: in the course of a speech personal expression in language and gestures increases and becomes stronger; the orator is ultimately 'carried away', while at the beginning there would often seem to be some slight hesitation.

In addition, the moments of highest expression are really always high points in an inwardly connected, meaningful series of movements. The ultimate in expression, where the learnt movement has almost become a purely expressive movement, is 'grace', and this cannot be consciously attained but comes with the flow of inner participation. A disturbance from the outside would, for example, bring an actor 'back to earth'; he would go on playing his part but the 'expression' would have suffered for a short while.

Accordingly, we must not work exclusively with exercises which are single movements the sequence of which depends only on the will of the teacher (resting, in good cases, on his opinion of the physical effect they will have) so that for the next movement the teacher's 'command' or the pupils' memory is always necessary. Meaningful sequences of movements are needed which develop step by step according to their own rules without interference by the teacher. These two different kinds of physical exercise must have equal priority in physical education as a whole. Examples of these two are the gymnastic tricks on apparatus in all their profusion and variety, and also athletic exercises and springboard diving: on the other side there is the great wealth of games and dances of all kinds.

This is not to say that individual expression cannot develop in the first type of exercise, the acrobatic forms. If such exercises are part of a training which supports the capacity for expression and is based on its preservation, they too will finally, when they have been mastered, bear the personal stamp of the person doing them. Nevertheless, for preserving the capacity for expression, 'play', the connected action of games and dances, is indispensable; it is the soil on which expression thrives best; it allows purely expressive movements to come into being and furthers the development of expression in voluntary movement.

A closer look at representation will clarify much, for only in the comparison between the two concepts are the differences strongly brought out. However, before this we must touch briefly on the question of the so-called rhythmic gymnastics which by many people are wrongly thought to be *the* means of expressive training. If they really were *the* means, the wonderful expressiveness of the movements of peasants in the Alps in their work and in their games, dancing and acting (paradise and passion plays) would be quite inexplicable. They have never done rhythmic gymnastics, nor have the primitive peoples whose movements are enviably genuine and beautiful. It would indeed be very strange if something as old and universally human as expressive movement and representation were to depend on rhythmic gymnastics, devised and developed in the twentieth century. The fact is that all really good physical education, past or present, was and is rhythmic, and that a special call for rhythmic exercise became necessary only when the feeling for human movement had degenerated so far that exercising was being done unrhythmically. For the exponents of modern gymnastics to have realized the need and made this call is worthy of merit, but in so doing they have fallen, in part, into the error of thinking that some exercises were rhythmic and some not, whilst actually it is only a question of a way of moving. The rhythmic element is a sign of all lively, natural movement, not only of that formed artistically. Rhythmic movement and artistically formed movement are not the same thing; they are to one another as the raw material is to the work of art made from it. As long as a person cannot move rhythmically he is incapable of framing a work of art in movement, but by moving rhythmically he is not yet creating a work of art; which leaves unanswered the question of how to distinguish the truly rhythmic from the seemingly so.

One of the worst errors in this matter is the idea that the character of rhythmic movement depends on its being set to music. The decisive mark of the rhythmic execution of a movement is not the combination of movement with music but its combination with breathing. Exercising to music or the beat of a tambourine is as unlikely to assure this as was the former way of doing exercises to counting. It is true that the dull, reverberating beat of drum or tambourine is less bad, it breaks up the movement less, but the idea that this alone guarantees that the movement will be rhythmic is one of the errors which goes back to the continual muddling up of rhythm and beat. True rhythm does not restrict itself to dance movement sequences but is found in all movements, in heavy physical work as well as in the highest sporting achievement.

If the preservation of the natural capacity for expression and the training of the ability to represent are thought to be part of the education of all people, then no solution is to be found in rhythmic gymnastics. Most experience in this aspect of education has up to now been gained in dance which is only one branch of physical education. From this specialized field it is impossible to understand a whole nation with its varied working life and just as varied recreations and joys, and without this understanding no generally valid form of physical education can be built up.

(b) *Representation*

Some passages from Klages (1921) will help to define the concept of representation:

The character of representation has two sides: emphasis of salient features and control of the total image.

However diverse borrowed traits may seem when looked at singly, they nevertheless always bear the expressive character of what is common to them: the wish to represent something.

The handwriting of one person is representational and stylized in its most important parts, but that of another is expressive and rhythmic. What distinguishes between the two ways of manifesting the inner life does so in every penstroke, every gesture . . ., in the posture, the tone of voice, the whole bearing, and even in that eternal outcome of human action: the productions of trade, art, and writing.

Thus from the great number of possibilities one chooses those which seem best to serve what one is trying to represent. What one is looking for is not expression but distinguishing factors. The will to represent, according to Klages, tends of necessity to stylize, it always puts things into a kind of order; when done best this is the evident and convincing order which one calls style. According to this, one could in a certain sense call the person representing something active, and the person expressing something passive.

Whilst expression is the involuntary, unconscious appearance of inner activity, representation is a conscious act. Thus in representation one can speak of practice, but not in expression. Representation and expression are two essentially different things, and the distinction between them is illuminated when one considers that animals carry out the latter, but only humans the former..

Representation is based on voluntary movements; it does not, as one might think, consist of a sequence of expressive movements but of learnt movement sequences. From the very beginning these are set in a special context, and they must be learnt and practised until they have become part of the actor. They then proceed by themselves when the cue for them is given, without the conscious mind again having to take part in every phase.

Consideration must be given here to the generally familiar 'transition of willed processes into fully automatic ones'. At first the conscious mind has to watch over each phase of a sequence of movements carefully and attentively; once it has been learnt, it happens without conscious effort, quite by itself. It becomes, as a very vivid phrase puts it, 'a part of one'; Klages translates this into the word 'vitalized' in order to bring out the essential features of the process and to oppose the incorrect and unnatural idea inherent in the term 'mechanized' or 'mechanical'. Life makes itself master of the movement sequence and it now appears as a purely expressive movement. Good acting is not mechanical but a phenomenon of life, and every phenomenon of life is animated, that is, it has expression.

The movement which has become automatic, 'the merely habitual movement, has the negative characteristic in common with the truly expressive one of happening unconsciously'. Nevertheless, as Klages proves thoroughly and convincingly in his criticism of Darwin's theories on expression, the habitual movement and the truly expressive movement are essentially different, and can always be distinguished by the fact that one is always learnt, the other never.

Now one might think that habitual movements would be highly unsuited to representing anything psychological or intellectual, because of being carried out mechanically without further thought, but daily experience teaches that this is not so. When an actor learns a role or a pianist a piece of music he can exploit it to the full (up to the limit of his personal talents) only when the movements have become automatic. Only the movement that has been thoroughly learnt is a suitable medium for representation.

It is the same in other skills of a more ordinary nature. When a person 'is just learning or has never fully learnt to use a fork when eating, to mount a horse, to dance, fence, row, swim, he cannot fully express himself in any of these actions, and we must learn to assess the extent of his lack of practice in order to discover his potential ability'. In other words: without practice we can never measure the extent of ability attainable by us in a certain field, indeed it is only by practising that we actually discover how far we can get. On the other hand, in every field there are certain limits beyond which we cannot go however hard we practise.

There are several forms of representation and all depend in the last resort on movement. So good physical education which increases the flexibility and grace of the body creates a good basis for all representation, and indirectly is of service to general acting ability. However, it is the special task of physical education to benefit the body so that only the forms of acting which have definite physical value should be cultivated. Physical education should not therefore be expected to cultivate acting forms which have no effect on the body, however valuable they may be in themselves.

Physically valuable forms of representation which have a part to play are:

> The imaginative games of children, various games using movement and jokes, and dancing in the widest sense of the word: in the form of singing games (which contain

many elements of acting), folk dances, dancing games, and whatever other kinds of dances one likes to distinguish.

One scarcely needs to say that the preceding observations concerning dancing refer only to the repetition of already existing dances. We do not wish to say anything against the original creation which results in artistic dancing, but generally this does not come under consideration for the work in physical education.

Klages states the fact that only the fully learnt movement is a suitable medium for representation in the following words: 'The voluntary nature of a movement can become subject to the total presentation of the personality . . .' This is the state which must be achieved in the representation if it is to be good. It is immediately obvious that this subjection can only happen, and the total presentation of the personality can only arise, when the actor immerses himself completely in the work allotted him. This is a feat of the imagination. The choice of activity in which children or adolescents or adults are able to immerse themselves will therefore depend on the development of their imagination. Individual differences in this are by no means small but an average, general line of imaginative development can be ascertained. Schools, which are schools for the masses, must take the average into account.

Our first task is therefore to get to know the development of imagination in children and young people for whom physical education is planned. In referring to Spranger's work *Psychology of Youth* (1924), two products of imagination can be distinguished: combination and illusion. In illusion insight is gained into certain forms by observing them and inanimate objects are animated; both these processes are aided by the still imprecise, imperfect perceptions of children. Combination is a very different matter and has to do with images, either selecting them from past experience and putting them in new situations, or as 'creative inspiration', making a new form enter directly into consciousness.

The stages of development through which imagination passes are described by Tumlirz in *Introduction to a Study of Youth*, (1920): 'The first phase of childhood—first to seventh year—is characterized by the imaginative illusion common to all children. With more precise observation of reality, and increasing interest in the external world, the illusionism, which is concerned only with the ego, disappears without the child's being capable of new achievements of combination. In general, the activity of imagination seems to be limited in the second period—up to puberty—and to apply itself more to serving the child's interest in the external world. Even in imaginative children imagination develops slowly at this time. Not until puberty, when the interest of young people is again centred on themselves, does the activity of imagination have another upsurge, then illusionism recedes in favour of combinative imagination. New kinds of imaginative creations become more frequent and the activities are better willed and planned.'

Therefore, when children 'act' it is obviously different from when an actor acts. Children's acting is a game of illusion, whilst in the case of the actor an artistic representation is taking place. Usually one does not call it acting in children but says that 'they are playing at doctors, teachers, coachmen, cooks, engine drivers or firemen'. The degree of consciousness is much less in them than it would be in an adult, who would try to represent where the child just plays; the child is, if not fully, at least much more at the level where 'the voluntary nature of the movement is of itself subject to the total presentation of the personality'. Of course the use of the word 'play' for the art of the actor points to a relationship between the two ways of representing, they are two levels of the same activity and one is tempted to apply to them what Kleist says in his *Marionette Theatre* (1810) about gracefulness: 'it appears in its purest form where one is most, or not at all, conscious of it'. In this case this would mean in the child and in the very talented actor. Various moving games and joking games provide another form of representation for children. Many catching games, for example, begin with a long dialogue; the catcher and the person he is pursuing exchange speeches before the chase begins. In other games a song or a saying supports the action between the catcher and the other players, who have to keep away from him until the point when the catcher is allowed to make his catch. Other games again, entail the guessing of what one or many players are pretending to be, and the word which solves the puzzle is the signal for general pursuit. Many verses and counting-out rhymes also provide the occasion for a kind of acting.

In this a phenomenon is to be seen which can also be observed elsewhere: that in childhood much is still undivided, whole, which is afterwards split up into different compartments. A true child's game really includes everything: it is a play, a dance, a fight, and various other things at the same time. The plots, conversations, rhymes and proverbs of genuine children's games are not of secondary importance to them; one takes something essential from the game by leaving them out and using only what could be called the athletic part, e.g. 'running after someone in order to catch him'. In this way the soul is taken out of the games, and the teacher is afterwards forced to search for a means of reviving them again. Unfortunately our age is so lost to instinct that it is in continual danger of going wrong when it attempts this.

Like the games of illusion these movement games have their place for a time, and because they are rich in content and finely graded they can be made use of over a fairly long period, but at a certain stage of development they become impossible. At the age which desires to conquer the world outside, when even imagination seems only to serve this purpose—from nine to about eleven—they are no longer of interest. The word 'real' is almost an estimation of value at this age, and so it is not to be wondered at if children want real actions even in games, and forsake childish games. On the one hand they turn to team games, which demand purposeful action and leave no time or strength for imagination, and on the other to teasing games. These too have real action. A player must carry out some humorous task by means of skill, readiness, speed, etc., whilst the others try to make it as difficult as possible for him within the limits set by the rules of the game. The first to try his luck is selected by casting lots or counting-out; after this it is the turn of anyone who has been caught out in some clumsiness or carelessness.

One can see that in these teasing games the element of testing one's powers is much stronger than in the children's games, and that the play of fantasy appears to be correspondingly pushed out. However, it is still present, surprise is often decisive in these games and with it of course pretence. One pretends, for example, not to be attending so as to take one's opponent by surprise;

if this is successful and one's part was well played one is relieved of the job and can watch the others being harrassed. It is scarcely necessary to give examples of these universally familiar games.

The teasing games keep their importance beyond childhood; unspoilt young people and adults get the same pleasure from them. There is an inexhaustible supply of these games; skill and presence of mind can be tested, with varying degrees of difficulty, in jokes which end in general laughter or in serious exertion.

Finally dancing, and its place in physical education with regard to expression and representation must be discussed. A dance is a sequence of movements which have to be learnt; the action of the dance is given in its main lines. Of course this is not what is important in it, it is only the skeleton. As a pianist never plays a piece of music exactly the same twice, so a dance is a little different each time. When it has become part of the dancer his life puts a different stamp on it each time, for life never presents two exactly similar moments. The movements are the same, but the movement pictures are different each time. The course of the dance in space and time is actually never the same but only similar.

In healthy, normally developed children it is probably always the case that they 'overlay the pattern with their own form'. According to Klages (1921) this is what constitutes a talent for a certain activity, and in this sense one can say that every child has a talent for dancing. Dancing is therefore an essential part of children's physical programme—but it must fulfil two requirements: the content of the dances must be suited to the age-group in question, and they must not be done for exhibition purposes. (Perhaps they should never be done for exhibition purposes, but for their own sake. This is a very far-reaching distinction which must not be overlooked.) Ambitious striving to get the children quickly to performance level is, at this stage more than at any other, a sin against life.

The dances must be chosen according to the children's level of understanding. Wooing dances for example, the content of which is courtship, in however veiled a form, are not suitable for children. This human relationship is not yet comprehensible to them and should not be so; no teacher can wish for precocity here, and he must therefore avoid furthering it in any way. The

impulse of true children's dancing is joy in movement, enjoyment of twirling round, hopping and jumping and twisting round.
Good examples of this are the round-dances whose climax,
always awaited with excitement, is when everyone suddenly sits
or falls down, and the bridge games with their endless procession
underneath.

Dancing remains delightfully unartificial and unforced
throughout childhood as long as the teacher retains a modest
and reverent attitude to the child's way of expressing himself.

Although in childhood the best direction is that which inter-
feres least, this is no longer true for the period of puberty. The
flowing joy in movement dries up, and the unimpeded self-
expression gives way to divided feelings in which a strong need
for self-expression is combined with an impulse to hide one's
feelings. The talent for dancing common to all children is now
by no means general. This form of expression is closed to many
young people; in others it may be present but stifled for the
time being by the physical clumsiness which almost always
occurs at this period. For this reason dancing must be considered
a form of representation which is difficult of access at the beginning of puberty. Spranger says somewhere that young people
choose for their artistic creativity the material which presents
them with the fewest difficulties; this is certainly not movement,
for the clumsiness of these years is proverbial.

This intermediate phase, where the self-containment and
assurance of the child is no longer present and the maturity of
the adult not yet, sets the educator a difficult and responsible
problem. A detour via consciousness is often the only way open
here, and reasoned exercising becomes a necessity. Details,
which were learnt unconsciously by children, can now be singled
out and practised separately. Much can be done with such exercises as, for example, fitting movements to music, emphasizing
their attack at the beginning, their ending, their force and speed;
also rhythmic movement to a drum or tambourine, etc. This
work creates technical ability which, when this most difficult
period of growth is past, will be a great help in dancing. This is
the time too for thinking out the inner structure of movement,
and awakening a feeling for good form. Only organically and
physically correct movements are a medium for artistic representation and since their anchorage in the subconscious is

usually lost at puberty, they must be regained by conscious effort.

One way of getting over the years between childhood and maturity, which are not rich in dancing, is careful movement training which places compliance with the laws of space—the constructive element in dance—in the foreground. Another way is to explore the musical elements and other forms of dance accompaniment. It depends entirely on the individual teacher which way he takes; taste and talents are what decide the matter.

The division between children's dancing and that of young people is in many cases extraordinarily sharp, in others it is less clear. This probably depends on whether the phenomena of puberty are quick and stormy, or slower and therefore less obvious. When the growth in height stops, the way of moving gradually settles down again, and then at least the physical hindrance to progress in dancing disappears.

Of course, the natural, almost universal talent for representation by means of movement has been lost. As is the case with other forms of representation a special talent is either present, or it is not, and insurmountable bounds are often clearly and painfully obvious. However, there are many more modest talents which can, with good direction, be brought to at least an understanding of the substance of representation, which their own unaided efforts could not have achieved.

The number of dances which can now be understood intellectually gets bigger and bigger. The introspection which occurs in these years, the understanding of one's own feelings as well as those of others, allows the comprehension of dances with inner rather than outer action. Whether the development is in the direction of the folk dance (more precisely, peasant folk dancing) or of artistic dancing depends on the pupils. Folk dancing would be as unsatisfying for some young people as the dancing games would be for others, depending on their intellect and culture.

These indications must suffice to show how much school children can gain from dancing. Only one further point must be made: dancing must be considered, especially during the period of transition from the child to the adult, as a means of self-education, not as a creation of works valuable in their own right.

In every kind of representation there is the risk that the part played by nature in the success of a work is underestimated and one's own part overestimated. Thus a beautiful voice may seem to designate someone for the career of a singer—and then it becomes clear that he will never get beyond the level of mediocrity because although the physical requirements are there the intellectual ones are not. The young person is not very capable of understanding this, especially when it concerns himself; he dreams of a brilliant career, the image of the celebrated actor or famous singer has an irresistible appeal. It is the same in dancing; but the dancer too requires more than a well-built, light and agile body and a little love of music. Attraction to the artistic calling of the dancer is not without risk; the words of Spranger (1924): 'the poorest of all mediocre artists is the mediocre actor' can reasonably and accurately be applied to the dancer, and especially to the female dancer.

Thus, not only for children but for young people too, one must guard against too many dancing performances, though practising for a performance is in some ways justifiable, for it provides an incentive to finish something completely. They learn to fight and battle to the bitter end with the work they have begun, as long as their strength holds out. From the point of view of the spectator the finished work is often trifling. The applause of the spectators, so often assumed by the performers to be for their artistic achievements, should really be given for industry and stamina. This misunderstanding endangers their capacity for artistic discrimination, which is only just beginning to develop and needs careful guidance. Yet to allow young people no claims to art would be to degrade them in intellect and soul.

Unfortunately nowadays there is less good tradition in dancing than in other arts, and therefore less general capacity for discrimination. Nowhere else has the worst rubbish a chance of finding admirers. This cannot be otherwise; after centuries of neglecting the body one cannot expect a general understanding for the organic correctness of movement, and yet this is a prerequisite for judging artistic dancing.

Dancing in its various forms is to be utilized in physical education with three provisos: the dances must correspond to the level of mental development. They must bear some relation to the pupils' own lives. Dancing must be a means of self-education, and the pupils too must be conscious of this.

Perhaps it is not superfluous to add that everything said here about expression and representation is valid for both boys and girls.

Representation has been used by teachers of gymnastics in the
past, and even today a teacher may stimulate the children's
imagination by suggesting the movement of an animal or a
worker in order to achieve a certain physical effect. To clarify
the use of representational work in gymnastics some examples
from the work of Thulin (1925) will be discussed. In his book,
Gymnastics for Small Children, the following examples are given:

Chopping with an axe. The axe is held with both hands, one hand in
front of the other, both loosely clasped, at about the height of the fore-
head. The tree trunk is placed a long way in front of the feet. 'Reach out
well as you chop!' Try to get the children, by means of suitable images,
to keep their knees as straight as possible. Also the trunk is inclined
so that the upper part of the back can still be kept straight.

Turning a whetstone. If the teacher herself demonstrates how she wants
this performed it can become a good exercise for forward inclination of
the body.

Throwing snowballs. The teacher demonstrates the final on-guard
position, with the weight on the back leg, the knee bent. When the
left leg is in front the snowball is thrown with the right hand and vice
versa.

Catching butterflies. 'Look at the pretty butterfly. Catch it—now!' The
hands clap together in front of the face and are then swung down sideways. The teacher points out a flying butterfly and it is caught in the
way described.

What conclusions can be drawn from these examples? One is,
of course, that Thulin is not concerned with achieving the exercise form which corresponds to the course of the actual movement as it occurs when work is being done. The exact indications
given for the exercises would be highly unfitted to achieving
this. Nobody wishing to chop up a tree trunk would place it 'a
long way in front of his feet'; without giving it any thought at
all he will stand at the distance which is best for his body and
the tool he is using. Nor will he keep his knees stretched but will
allow them to give with the movement. This requirement is as
unjustifiable, from the point of view of the work to be done, as

the precept not to bend so far that the back cannot be kept straight.

The examples of throwing snowballs and catching butterflies show that in these exercises too their actual natural form is not the end, for no child throws snowballs ending up in the on guard position but merely passes through some similar position for a moment as he raises his arm; and no child catches a butterfly according to the description 'by clapping the hands together in front of his face and then letting them fall down sideways' for this would harm the butterfly, perhaps even kill it. (Children should be educated to revere all living creatures, so this exercise of the imagination is very unfortunate. Catching butterflies is in itself a questionable pastime and in this form it is really completely barbaric.)

Thus, for Thulin the aim was not the form of chopping, throwing, catching, etc., which occurred in life. From the detailed instructions for the exercises, the desired form was obviously the one with a definite effect on the body, as, for example, a stretching of the back of the legs or a straightening of the back. Because this goal was not comprehensible or interesting enough for a child, an attempt was made to create a reference to his way of thought by means of a label.

Thulin held that certain exercises (but not the everyday movements of life) could be expected to improve posture when they were carried out according to strict instructions as to their form. Children had to do these exercises with a defined form as early as possible, and to make them palatable an appeal was made to the imagination even though the movements were not performed in the natural manner. The children were not to be left with the way of moving peculiar to them but had to be brought to the allegedly more valuable movements with a defined form. The question of whether this is of general validity in physical education will not be discussed here but it is certainly not right for children, who derive more benefit from rich, natural, 'untidy' movement.

The principle of telling the children *what* they must do but not *how* they must do it excludes exercises with a defined form for both teacher and pupils. Avoiding the demonstration of exercises also works to the same end. The children's natural way of moving must be retained because this best helps their development. Plenty of varied individualistic movement is the daily bread of this age group and should not be replaced by any cleverly devised exercises.

For example, if the teacher makes the children pretend to chop wood he must aim at the method of execution which appears to be the best in real wood chopping. A child does it wrong, or rather, awkwardly, if he sets about it the wrong way —perhaps stands too far away or too near—or if he does not let the movement swing through his whole body, keeping his knees stiff, or if he does not fit his breathing in with the work so that his stamina suffers. If the teacher makes them pretend to throw snowballs he just tells them to throw high or far or at some goal, and he leaves it to each child to decide how to throw. He has to show 'a better way' only to very clumsy children who still have not come upon the best method after repeated throws.

What determines the method of execution is thus not the picture the teacher has of the movement but the demands made by the work. It does not matter how the teacher has arrived at his idea of chopping, throwing, etc., whether by tradition or his own observation: as an adult he can never guess at the child's movement well enough to be able to show it to him for he is at too great a distance from it. This is the main reason why adults should not demonstrate exercises to children.

Whilst correcting faults, nothing in contradiction to the actual work movement must be demanded, however advantageous it may seem from the point of view of the desired result, even if, for example, it were certain to stretch some joint; if this is absolutely necessary—which is not at all easy to decide—it must be attained in some other way, not by 'falsifying' a work movement.

The essential difference, therefore, in the use of the work movement, or rather its representation—for there is no question of its being actual life—in the examples given from Thulin's work for the children, is that Thulin's gymnastics aimed at movements with a defined form. He tried to make them comprehensible to the children by naming them after a similar work movement, instead of considering the various individual solutions to the problem to be correct as long as they were, from the point of view of the work to be done, practical.

Besides the representational type of exercises for children there are the total movement exercises (see above p. 98).

These too are everyday movements from life and thus suitable for children. They depend much less on the imagination.

Examples of these are:

> Lying on the back and turning on to the front; twisting round in a circle whilst jumping or running; kneeling down without moving one's feet; sitting or lying down without using one's hands, etc.

These total movements give an impression of what is to be done but leave the method of execution to each individual. They have an advantage over representational exercises because in nearly every class there are children who do not co-operate inwardly in the representational exercises; they are embarrassed and cannot escape from themselves. They do not then derive the fullest benefit from the exercises because they are not co-operating mentally. Representational exercises also demand a certain mood in both teachers and pupils; they border on the realm of artistic creation, even if in a childish form, and are thus not always successful. The individual child should also be given more freedom whilst doing them than is usually possible in gymnastic lessons. One cannot ever therefore build up a system of gymnastics for children in school on representational exercises alone.

To compare the use of representational movements with partial movements (see glossary) which may be necessary even in children's gymnastics: if one notices the same fault in many children in a class, for example, round shoulders, one can search for representational or total movements which are capable of reducing or removing them. In many cases this will be possible but sometimes a teacher cannot find a movement from life which corrects the fault effectively. Instead of twisting such a movement into a form in which it may 'take effect' it is better to carry out movements the only purpose of which is compensatory. Such exercises are justified simply by stating their purpose. By the time they go to school children are mentally developed enough to co-operate although only, of course, when they have complete confidence in their teacher—which is the fruit of thoroughly planned, satisfying work. However, the compensatory work must not predominate; movements from life and partial movements may be considered as in the same proportion as daily bread and medicine.

To sum up, one can say the following about the use of representational exercises and total movements; they are not disguised compensatory exercises but, without reservations or limitations, movements from real life, and we insist on this to the uttermost, indeed even to the paradoxical yet true statement: the child knows how to carry out the movement better than the teacher. The child, with his feeling for movement, can see it far better than the adult who is often exposed to error. The movements from life are the 'daily bread' of gymnastics and must therefore constitute the greater part of the exercises. Partial movements should be included because they are indispensable for compensatory work. Representational movements have their place in gymnastics for primary school children but total movements, which use everyday movements, are more generally useful as they do not depend to the same extent on the imagination of the teacher and the children.

19 Dancing play with movement

> The aesthetic attitude is not something which is only added to
> life as an afterthought in the shape of art and could just as well
> be missing, but is a shaping force of life itself. Art is only the
> highest form of this phenomenon which penetrates and trans-
> figures our whole existence.
>
> H. Nohl (1935)

In his system of physical education based on the purpose of
the exercises being done, Gaulhofer (and Streicher, 1922) cites,
along with achievement exercises, exercises for good form,
compensatory exercises and art of movement, and he subdivides
the last into the acrobatic arts (agility exercises, vaulting,
tumbling, gymnastics tricks on apparatus) and the dancing arts.
These have no practical value, are not even potentially useful;
they cannot be measured but only evaluated, and the question of
taste about which, as we all know, it is impossible to argue, at
once enters into this evaluation. Fitting them into educationally
constructed work demands different categories from work which
remains in the realm of purposeful movement. Of the two art of
movement groups, dancing presents the most problems, and this
alone will be dealt with here.

In the first place movement is the means of moving around
within the environment in various ways (walking, running,
jumping, mounting, climbing) and of changing the surroundings
by using the hands (pulling, pushing, lifting, carrying, throwing). So movement is useful, it serves to keep men alive.
Similarly speech, in the first place, serves as a means of communication. Beyond this, movement and speech are expressive;
through them man can 'say what he suffers' and 'what makes
him happy', he can use them symbolically to gratify his desire
to represent the perfection of beauty. So, beyond usefulness,
movement and speech have another function in life; they become
material for artistic shaping; through them the realms of dancing
and poetry come into being.

Physical education must take both developments into account.
Just as simple communication, the clear message, must not be
missed out of language lessons, so useful, purposeful movement

must be schooled; people must be capable of moving well in ordinary life and work. Further, just as language lessons are incomplete if they do not also lead to the art of poetry, dancing is a legitimate part of the exercise material in physical education for it has 'a universal basis in human nature' (Pestalozzi, 1807). It must not be taught as though separated from the rest of the material, for this would make the fruitful interplay between purposeful and artistic movement impossible. It would be like entrusting one teacher with essays, spelling and grammar but another with the transition to poetry. Such a unified field of human life must not be torn apart; one part carries, includes, and delimits the other.

There is also the fact that—as already mentioned—precisely here lie the educational problems. As long as movement is tied to objectivity, directed at a necessary end, there is little danger of running off the rails, but a great deal of teaching skill is needed to handle movement as a material for shaping, for artistic creation; only fundamental thinking can lead to clarity.

'In the first place we have to come to terms with beauty of movement, its interplay in the moving group, and the flow in time', says Gaulhofer. In physical education we cannot go further since dance as a work of art is not a proper task for the school. Even Pestalozzi says that one should not try to create fencers and dancers (and one could add singers, violinists, etc.), but people who fence and dance.

So one must remember that it is always a question of lay dancing, and always of group dancing, never solo dancing.

Since social dancing too is eliminated by this consideration the great realm of the art of movement in dance has already become a lot smaller.What comes under consideration for physical education can now be divided into two groups: dancing and dancing play with movement.

From the traditional material children's round dances and singing games can be used, and they often contain acting elements besides those of dancing. From about the age of nine when the children enter the realistic phase, the dances must provide lively movement without representation. For this age up to puberty there is a large stock of dances suitable for children.

For the period of puberty one has first to make a very careful choice from the wealth of national dances; dances in couples with a strong erotic tinge are unsuitable for this age group. One can also choose neutral forms, that is those without a special stamp or social emphasis, from the wealth of European folk dances as long as they seem adapted to the feeling for movement of young people. Many dances might perhaps be a little changed for use in schools, as occasionally happens with games.

New creations suitable for this age group will be discussed later. First of all it is a question of the ready-made traditional dances which are learnt and danced as songs are learnt and sung. With them the first consideration is to make a correct choice. One has to take into account the mental character of the various age-groups, the environment and with it the intellectual horizon of the pupils, the degree of skill in movement already reached, perhaps also the profession towards which they are growing up. Educational tact is needed to find the right answer in individual cases.

Dancing play with movement is the real theme of this essay. Gaulhofer (and Streicher, 1930) writes:

This is not yet dancing, but it does have the task of teaching the pupils how to shape individual and group movement. The old art forms of gymnastics, exercises performed to command and the free standing exercises used for display, can no longer serve. . . . What we can use, because it has grown out of the feeling for movement of our own age, has been created by the modern gymnastic systems.

In order to avoid confusion the 'modern gymnastic systems' will be referred to by the term *Gymnastik* (see glossary). Those who know how *Gymnastik* came into being and developed are not surprised that it was this which threw a bridge over into art. It is not by chance but by intention that the report on the *Gymnastik* Conference in Berlin in 1923 bears the title 'Künstle-rische Körperschulung' (Artistic Body Training). As early as 1905 at the Art Education Day in Hamburg, and repeatedly later, *Turnen* and *Sport* were reproached with being so far removed from art. New paths were now taken especially in the movement forming exercises (see glossary); human movement is considered as a precious material which must be handled delicately and carefully because it has its own 'form'. This 'form' must not have violence done to it by exaggerated demands for achievement or instructions laid down by tradition. The striving for organically correct, 'pure' movement is one of the most important contributions which *Gymnastik* has made to present-day physical education.

It is true that the representatives of *Gymnastik* have always emphasized that human education, not dancing, is the goal but dancing happens to be a part of this, if not dance as a great art.

Gymnastik has a stronger artistic streak than the other historical-sociological forms of physical exercise. However, one must not forget that *Gymnastik* came into being at a time when intellectualism in education was being sharply attacked on principle from other sides too, and that it was at that time that the educational possibilities of art were discovered. Books criticizing the cultural life of the time and the endeavours of societies such as 'Dürerbund' (Dürer Society) and 'Deutscher Werkbund' (German Society of Arts and Crafts) characterize the whole great movement for genuineness, objectivity and quality; the battle against trash and bombast in the field of architecture, the home, apparatus and clothing, all fall into this period. Education through art, education for art, formation of taste, cultivation of the powers of shaping in place of overestimation of knowledge, cultivation of the ability to express oneself—these are the characteristic slogans of this period, and these intellectual currents carried *Gymnastik* with them. No wonder that human movement too began to be seen differently. The changes in clothing, especially that of women, probably also played a part in this. The human body could be seen, and this would previously have been considered unbecoming.

At first the physical education of this period remained untouched by these ideas. Here the desire for health ruled; doctors emphasized the necessity for plenty of movement outdoors and the care of posture. The games movement and the knowledge of Swedish gymnastics were stronger influences than *Gymnastik* with its questions of form.

The parallel with handicrafts can bring greater understanding. The urge for adornment, the desire for beauty, are powerful forces in human beings. It is not enough that useful objects should fulfil their purpose, they must also be beautiful. In an earthen jug the functionally important place where the body gives way to the neck is emphasized and decorated by regularly spaced finger impressions. Even in type, impersonal as it is, the repeated asterisks which divide sections have the effect of a decoration. The ornament develops as a division of a surface. The things which surround us daily are seldom nakedly practical. The vase has to be noble in form and beautiful in colour. The belt must go with the dress, the brooch is supposed to hold something together, but they must both also give a final touch to the whole effect by being contrasted or matched in colour. A chair which is not comfortable to sit on, a handle which does not feel good to the hand, is not beautiful. A heavy dark frame does not suit a delicate drawing in pastel. The connection between what is right and what is beautiful is here very clear.

So the beauty of movement too is now seen and it is to be emphasized, not submerged in achievement. In movement nothing is beautiful which contradicts the meaning of the movement: 'The material shows the limits and defines what is forbidden' (Heuss, 1951). Those who run only with the stop-watch, battling grimly for better speeds, do not experience 'the wave-like motion of running' (Loheland) which is part of its nature, so they know only one side of running. Those who consciously experience the peculiar dynamics of a jump gain a familiarity with jumping which in the final resort also helps them to achieve more. This is probably the reason why athletics nowadays have adopted 'rhythmic' exercising so enthusiastically, even for men.

Making an object which is both practical and beautiful is very important: the need for it to be useful means objectivity, soberness, and is a protection against sentimentality and extravagance. The possibility of making an objective evaluation is equally salutary for teacher and pupils. On the other hand artistic shaping is a necessary counterbalance to materialism and the overestimating of quantity. It leads to the question of form. The analogy with physical exercise is clear: purposeful movement is indispensable in forcing one to be objective. Yet objectivity is not enough; movement can also be beautiful and it should be beautiful, not by adding decorations but by working out what is essentially beautiful in it. In physical education, physiology is not enough because it does not consider or take seriously questions of form but takes only material factors into account.

We are indebted to Fritz Klatt (1930) for a very fine exposition of the significance of personal artistic efforts. What, he asks, is the meaning of the urge to shape things artistically? 'Shaped expression is recognized as the primeval way out of the

tribulations of life, and is to a certain extent possible for everyone.' For artistic shaping, however, there is only one preparatory
education. 'The craft aspect of art, practice in handling the
material in which the work of art appears, can be taught. That is,
the correct handling of stone and clay, of colour, movement and
words can be learnt.' Besides this, self-management such as working oneself up to creative tension, can be learnt. Of course neither
assures one of artistic shaping. 'To everyone who practises, it
remains a mystery how the work of art comes into being from
the correct fitting together of the materials of harmony, rhythm
and thought-structure.' Inspiration has to be there too: 'Everyone who wishes to create something needs this triad of ability—
mastery of the material, self-discipline and inspiration'.

The preparatory forms of dancing give the pupil familiarity
with the material of movement. One achieves this familiarity
only by actually moving; similarly it means much more musically
to play oneself than to listen to others.

It is a great advantage that movement is a transitory material.
The 'works of art' which come into being through these attempts at
shaping cannot be put behind glass and they cannot be given away
as presents and even if they fail, at least the children have moved.

The preparatory forms of dancing begin without a sharp
transition from the formative exercises (see glossary); these
alone are a sure enough foundation on which to build.

Examples of this exercise material are:

> Walking, running and jumping to various rhythms;
> walking and running in groups arranged in space; throw-
> ing and catching tricks with balls, batons, clubs, hoops,
> ropes, etc.; swinging legs, arms and the trunk, also in
> patterns and sequences in time and space, and with the
> use of hand apparatus; pulling and pushing in playful
> forms; jumping in pairs and in small groups.
>
> A few traditional dancing games can be included and
> the pupils can also try to make up simple dancing games
> to music, set or improvised, if it seems right for them and
> they enjoy it.

To compare these preparatory forms with another art may
help to make the work clear. They could be compared with the

technical exercises of instrumental playing, with runs, thirds, sixths, octaves, broken chords, etc. They return in the pieces of music or rather they have been separated out of the pieces of music and now they are practised, proceeding chromatically or diatonically, modulating into related keys, with rhythmic variations, so that they are ready for all occasions. To give an example in movement: the teacher can get pupils to work in pairs with a crossed arms hold and to do a twisting jump travelling the whole length of the gymnasium, telling them to feel the characteristic rhythm of this double game and to work it out neatly. Each pair can do this on its own, or a beat with a tambourine can be provided to which all must conform.

In these preparatory forms one is moving in the no-man's land between formative exercises (see glossary) and creative movement and, whilst teaching, one often changes from one to the other. Seeing faults in the pupils one returns to work on good form and posture, and as the pupils mature one progresses, for example, by bringing them together into a moving group.

For, just as good movement form is a prerequisite for creative movement, so attempts at creative movement themselves demand good form. When one can hear what importance a run has musically in a piece of music, or a percussive sequence of chords, or a muted accompaniment with broken chords, one plays them better. And when a thing is repeated regularly the faults in it often straighten themselves out. So for example Robert Schumann says of one of his studies (opus 3, for piano): 'It is easier to learn this by playing it through than by practising a few sections of it with too much care'.

By means of regularly alternating jumps to either side, the differences between left and right often practically level out; again it is sometimes easier to fall into the swing in a group than alone. In rhythmic progressive jumps one learns to fit in to a certain time, and this gives one a finer feeling for the onset of the leap and for the fluid transition between running and jumping. So one could work on a running jump as if one were doing it over a real obstacle: take-off corresponding to the form and height of the obstacle, free flight over it, elastic landing, and fluid run-on. The individual has to work on bringing out all these factors of good form. Now this running jump can become the theme of a movement game; two pupils do it in time side by side. At first they emphasize only the rhythmic regularity, and then the spatial regularity too, by doing the jumps whilst meeting and parting. It is not the space available which determines the sequence; the two do not move 'through space', over the obstacle, but 'in space' in a sequence which they have themselves chosen. Music could be improvised to go with this, or at least a rhythmic accompaniment on the tambourine, but even without any accompaniment the course of the movement and its conclusion can be worked out by attention to what the other person is doing.

So one would arrive at a movement structure which could be likened to a study, a sketch, or an étude. It already has a musical form, occurring in a certain key, and in rhythmic symmetry with beginning, climax and ending. In this way it would not just be a traditional dance which would be learnt but a new dance would be created. This form of creative work corresponds to work done in other subjects; the pupils write essays, in drawing they not only copy but also practise free 'sketching', and even in music lessons they occasionally 'compose'. 'Productive creation is considered by experienced art teachers as the most fruitful foundation for an understanding of art' (Pallat, L., 1930). These improvised dances, which can be retained if they are successful and used to enrich the stock of dances for young people, can be termed 'dancing games'. The term is short and generally comprehensible; it is not yet laid down as a technical term, and well defines the distinction between the dances newly formed out of the feeling for movement of our own age and the traditional dance forms of earlier ages. The word 'game' also points to the modesty with which such new creations must be considered; they are not works of art but games in the material of movement which, like the voice, is undoubtedly one of the oldest and most generally accessible materials for artistic activity. The dancing games result from communal work in which the stimulus and leadership lie sometimes more with the teacher and sometimes more with the pupils. For creative attempts of this kind music is probably indispensable; without its swinging, relaxing and regulating power scarcely anything can be achieved in school. Such attempts at creation belong to the period when the pupils have become mature enough to understand, to a certain degree, the meaning of 'form' in art.

It is important to find a good solution to the problem of the music. Gramophone records are not satisfactory. Sometimes a well-tuned piano in the school hall can be used; pianos do not belong in the gymnasium, they take up space and can never be kept well tuned. The best answer would be little 'orchestras' with changing players—one instrument for the melody (a recorder for example) with a tambourine and other percussion instruments to accentuate the rhythm. For this, however, it would be essential for the music and physical education teachers to collaborate closely.

These attempts at creative dance to suitable music are possible but they are not obligatory for every class and every teacher, and the word 'attempts' indicates that good results cannot be achieved under all circumstances. The requisite qualities (musicality, musical training) may be lacking in the teacher but also in the class; there are classes which do not respond, and such things cannot be forced. The teacher then has to be satisfied with the preparatory dance forms, which must never be omitted and which in themselves have great formative value.

These attempts at creation have a prospect of success only if they follow careful preparation. Children must have plenty of their own types of dances as long as their attitude to movement is naïve. The period of puberty, much poorer in dance, must be used conscientiously for work on good movement form, not just for achievement—which naturally also requires good form—but in order to become familiar with the special dynamics and the space and time factors of human movement. The playful forms of running and jumping, pulling and pushing, and the various tricks with movable apparatus must be allowed plenty of practice. Side by side with this work, ready-made traditional dances must be danced, and their form experienced.

In these attempts at creation the teacher must be satisfied if a craftsmanlike, neat thing is produced, a creation with inner cohesion, with parts which fit in with one another and are combined into a whole without breaks, so that in the variety of movements unity is visible. It does not matter that traditional dances are often the model. The teacher must keep a 'trial and error' attitude of mind, be open to ideas contributed by the pupils, and, in fact, always ready to pick up and make use of good ideas. Whatever is unsuccessful has served its purpose and is not preserved; its value lies in the work which has been done on it, but it has no objective value and is not worth handing down to posterity.

Above all, real movement themes must be used and no inorganic mixture made of compensatory exercises, acrobatic pieces and dance themes. From alternate bending and stretching one can make display exercises but not a dancing game, even if they are done in time on a lighted stage. Such 'pictures' may ravish harmless spectators, especially proud parents, but are quite valueless and certainly do not lead to the understanding of a work of art constructed in the material of movement.

The teacher has to choose carefully, and what is taken over must be 'built in'. This means that everything must fit in with the educational principles of physical education and beyond this, with the school. One cannot tell the artist what he can or must do—time judges his work; but the teacher who uses physical exercise as a means of training must be selective. Not everything that exists can be used.

Finally, what are the main educational principles which must govern everything? All dancing movement must apply biologically sound stimuli. So everything which has no physiological effect must be excluded, even if it is in itself quite beautiful and good. This prevents one from, for example, overstepping into the field of musical education. Most schools nowadays have too little time for physical exercise so none of it must be given away.

The connection with the other school subjects must never be lost. If efforts are being made to train the ear of the pupils, an untuned piano must not make a travesty of musical enjoyment in the dance lesson. One must keep to the level of quality of the other arts which the school is trying to introduce. Pupils who are to learn to understand Shakespeare, Hardy and T. S. Eliot should not hop about like savages in the dance lessons. In dance education the cross references to history and the cultivation of the arts are especially important.

Dancing as a whole, that is dancing games with their preparatory forms and the dances themselves, must obey the same laws of form as all the rest of the work. If one insists that the feet be kept straight when standing still and moving, this must also hold good for dancing. If exaggerated flexibility of the joints is rejected and the norm is shown to be correct, then deep back-bends, the splits, etc., must be eradicated from dancing too. Peculiar and grotesque movement is no material for the school, even in the guise of dancing; above all it does not constitute a standard for physical good form. Everything contrary to the dignity and nobility of humanity must be avoided. And one must also avoid slipping into sugariness and trash, especially with girls. Everything to do with dancing belongs to art education and so must not fall out of this framework.

In the introduction to his fine book *Aesthetic Reality* (1935) Nohl says: 'nobody will find out how he should write his poems or paint his pictures from aesthetics, but he will learn to understand the world of aesthetics'. Aesthetics can even 'help to lead to a new strictness of the artistic conscience', they can 'increase the clarity of the artistic will'.

To such a salutary state of mind this essay is intended to lead, and not to a direct introduction to dancing play with movement which, despite all the happiness and lightness proper to young people, is safely founded only on serious, indeed strict, movement training.

Physical exercise plays a much greater part in school education
than it used to. Fitting great new fields of exercise into the
physical education programme is not always easy to organize,
and often there is friction with teachers of other subjects. Physical education cannot always be expected to withdraw its claims.
Where these are justified they must be supported, otherwise
physical education stops serving the children's welfare; but it is
not only changing the organization of physical education which
gives rise to many possibilities of friction—reforming the work
from inside does too. Many difficulties can easily be removed by
just clarifying concepts, explaining what is really meant. Others
will always remain because personal views on this or that in
educational questions can never be quite eliminated. However,
even with these ultimately unanswerable questions it is useful
to discuss them because this at least narrows the circle of matters
in dispute. Such a question which has long needed discussing is
that of achievement.

In general, physical education teachers want 'more achievement' and justify this by pointing out that without making correspondingly high demands for achievement they cannot fulfil
their task of training their pupils. The other teachers usually
want 'less achievement'; in the first place they fear physical
damage, secondly, over-fatigue of the pupils which might make
them less capable of or less keen on intellectual achievement, and
finally, they are worried lest psychologically the pupils become
victims of the desire for physical success.

How can this conflict be resolved? Is high achievement
absolutely necessary to physical education, so that it must be
attained at any price, even that of the 'soul's salvation'? Or is
the 'salvation of the soul' of such inestimable value that it must
be bought even at the cost of complete physical development?
Or is there indeed, an alternative here—is it perhaps possible,
by using this means of development correctly, to have the indispensable high achievement without any physical or psychological damage? Then one could no longer reject achievement

altogether and call it bad but would have to see that it, like other means, can be well applied or misused.

The first fear—that lasting harm can very easily be caused to the heart, for example, by physical achievement is easily re-moved. Investigations have shown that there can be no question of a real effect on the heart, let alone harm, in people who play 'games or sports for pleasure'. Physical education with its limita-tions can, in the best cases, be considered as 'sport for pleasure'. With three periods of exercise a week in which classes of thirty to forty pupils have to be kept busy, often in limited space, it is not so easy to overdo it. However, when a pupil has suffered some damage it must be investigated carefully to find out whether it really was caused by the work at school. For example, in a case where physical education was reproached with causing a splay-foot, closer examination revealed that the pupil concerned had been 'training intensively' for a long time in a school of dancing, which was more likely to have been the cause.

It is not disputed that even in physical education the demands for achievement can be set too high by ambitious or stupid teach-ers and that this can cause damage, but in general, given the present time allowance and the available space, the danger of physical damage caused by over-high achievement cannot be con-sidered very great.

Naturally this does not dispose of the second objection, that pupils use energy for the physical achievements which they then do not have for the academic subjects. It is, of course, putting the matter too simply to imagine that the pupils could and would without more ado put all the energy not used physically into their academic work. Yet even if one imagines that everyone has a certain amount of energy at his disposal which he can share between intellectual and physical achievements as he wishes, it is still an open question whether it is really best to use up all the energy on intellectual achievements. Have teachers the right to insist that as little energy as possible is used in physical activities? To find a sensible answer to this question the impor-tance of achievement must be discussed a little more thor-oughly.

What are the real reasons for the teacher of physical educa-tion being keen on his pupils running a great deal, running swiftly and without tiring; on their learning to jump not only over 60 cm but over 1 metre 20 cm; on their being able to throw or hit a heavy ball a long way; on their being able to perform a difficult vault over the box? The result of the exercises means nothing to the teacher. Whether a ball lies here or there, whether the pupil stands on this side of the box or the other—considered as a result, this is a matter of indifference to everyone except to the pupil who has thrown or vaulted. To ignore all the intellectual or psychological effects and consider only the physical aspects, what it means to the teacher is that the pupil's metabolism has been stimulated by the movement, that his heart and lungs have worked harder than usual, that his vital organs have been stimulated to increased activity. And if these increased demands are repeated often enough the result is that they gradually adapt themselves to the increased demands, they work better, and their nature is altered to comply with circumstances.

So when high achievement is demanded of the pupils in physical education it is done with the intention of creating a reaction in the body. Like all living things man has the capacity to adapt functionally. Living tissue becomes better, not worse, for having demands made on it; it regenerates itself where machine parts wear away. Lack of usage makes the organs atrophy. It is simply a biological law: the organs must be made to work. Especially in the case of growing human beings, the necessary formational stimuli must be introduced, if the best possible development is to be achieved according to the predisposition of each. Thus the demand for achievement constitutes an indispensable stimulus to growth.

Stimuli must be at a certain level if they are to be effective; subliminal stimuli are wasted. Stimuli that are too strong cause damage. There is an optimum level of stimulus: it stimulates strongly but does no damage. So one can see that the secret of using achievement correctly in physical education lies in its gradation; the right level has to be found.

Yet this gradation is not easy. How can one tell whether a stimulus is too high or too low? One can only deduce this from the pupil's reaction to it. A child is playing with others at 'catch' —he becomes breathless and turns red, he stands still and rests for a moment and then runs off happily again. The same child is running a longish distance as quickly as possible; he is seen to turn pale, and his pulse not only quickens but perhaps actually becomes irregular. Undoubtedly the first stimulus was appropriate but the second was too high.

From mass examinations of a few measurable achievements we know the average level of achievement of particular age-groups. Besides the scientific value of such work, this has direct value for the teacher; from it he knows whether he is dealing with normally developed children. If deviations from these standards of achievement are very great the teacher must decide where the reason lies. Is it in the special home conditions of the children—for instance, lack of space for movement in the city? Is it because the places for exercise at school are very bad—a small hall, in which adequate movement is not possible despite all the efforts and methodical skill of the teacher? Or is the teacher responsible, perhaps by one-sided work and neglect of important groups of exercises?

However, such average achievements do not give as much help as might be thought in determining the level of achievement to be sought. The fact that eleven-year-old boys run a distance of 60 metres in so many seconds says nothing about whether this distance is in itself suitable for the age-group. Again, this can only be decided by observing the pupils as they run. And then external conditions only need to be particularly bad (crosswind when running or throwing, bad ground) and the number of boys for whom the average achievement appears to be precise becomes incorrect; the pupils' achievement was really very good but the numerical results are much lower than would have been achieved under better external conditions. The good achievement of a pupil is not always represented by a high score. All these measurements of achievements too easily lead the teacher to a belief in numbers. He judges his work by the scores attained and in many cases he judges it wrongly.

The only justification for measuring achievement is when this confirms that the pupils have made progress. Since a school always uses the same place for exercise, a part, at least, of the external circumstances remains constant. One can note down obvious differences such as bad weather, then measurements taken throughout the year can give a picture of the pupils' progress and can spur them on to work at improving their own standards. For this is what counts: a pupil who at first could jump only 60 cm with difficulty and who gradually with industrious practice brings this to 120 cm has achieved something; another, who jumps 120 cm both at the beginning and the end of the year, has made no progress.

It can never be right to base evaluation, or the school report in physical education, solely on measurements. There is a tendency at the present time to judge people only by their outward achievements which may be justified in business life but not in the school.

Here lies the danger for physical education of competitive sports such as athletics and swimming. These competitive sports are based upon measurable achievement. Since the general public knows from the daily papers about this kind of physical exercise the opinion easily grows up that there is no other way of doing physical exercise; everything else is not to be taken seriously and is child's play. Whatever does not reach into the zone of the higher achievements, does not at least approach some record, seems of no consequence.

It is not always easy for physical education to preserve its educational position with regard to sport, and not to seem inferior because it cannot bear comparison with sporting successes. One has to learn to forget world records and think only of the pupils—to appreciate achievement not only for itself but as the achievement of one particular pupil. Moreover, the harmfulness of the sporting attitude for young people growing up and being educated does not lie only in the fact that it distorts their ideas of value but also that striving for achievement can cause damage to the body. Even when, by means of very careful education, one succeeds in avoiding all harm, this specialized training in sport is inadequate for thorough physical education. Ascertaining the world record is only possible by international comparisons. This in turn makes it necessary to determine precisely the external conditions under which the 'sporting competitions' take place, otherwise the results would not be comparable. So trying to decide 'how high one can jump' is necessarily bound up with the standardization of exercise, grounds and apparatus and, even worse, of forms of exercise. Athletes learn a certain technique and only that. This technique becomes senseless once the external conditions are changed. So, for example, a sprinter would be very unhappy if instead of running in special shoes on a cinder track he had to run barefoot in a meadow; he might still be first, even under these conditions, but the length of time he took would not be a record. Or the technique of hurdling: if one alters the distance between the hurdles the whole technique becomes senseless. The ideal place for competitive swimming is not the river or lake with unexpected currents and eddies, with stones and other obstacles, but the well equipped swimming pool with smooth walls, the warmed, calm water at the same temperature throughout, the familiar depth.

All this means a great impoverishment of exercise forms, just as laying down definite patterns for particular gymnastic tricks can lead one to consider all other 'unofficial' forms as incomplete.

There is another type of sport that Brücke (1926) defines in which unexpected obstacles have repeatedly to be overcome. One of the best examples of this is skiing off the beaten track. This is 'sport' in a quite different sense than, for example, athletics from which the above examples were taken. It resists standardization strongly by its special requirements and has been to a great extent successful in this. In skiing the achievement lies in the battle with wind and weather, with the changing terrain and the snow, in overcoming the variety of difficulties by the use of all one's powers, not just the physical ones, and applying one's abilities under continually changing conditions. For sound growth and development of young people this rich, varied, biological achievement is much more important than the restricted achievement of competitive sport.

Nevertheless, the sporting attitude to achievement has given us something of value. By achievement one used to understand the ability to do certain exercises, one evaluated the amount of strength and skill. Competitive sport has again focused attention on those other achievements (such as the various forms of running) which entail 'organic achievement', that is they make great demands on heart and lungs. Since these exercises are of great importance in childhood and adolescence, we have sport to thank for an important element in the reshaping of physical education.

Achievement, even when understood from a physical point of view only, is not simple and can thus never be fully expressed by a number. A person's capacity for achievement is not assured just because he is very good in one field, such as strength. He may be deficient in other fields. Complete physical training means that the capacity for achievement is many-sided, not limited, but this also means that achievement cannot be raised to the highest possible level in any one direction; this could happen only at the cost of variety. The different kinds of achievement can only co-exist at medium levels, the highest levels exclude one another. The sprinter, for example, may not ski because this makes his legs too strong and firm; the discus thrower may not row for a similar reason—providing of course that they are specialists. Anyone who sprints or throws the discus for pleasure can of course do whatever else he wants to, but then he cannot reckon on setting up a record.

In physical education we do not train 'specialists', and exercise and achievement are only the means to an end, not an end in themselves. Medium achievement in each particular field is more important than the highest in one field, because this can be attained only at the cost of the others. A capacity for many-sided achievement is an important goal in physical education, whilst from the point of view of sport it is an impediment.

After these reflections of a more basic nature we turn again to physical education; biological achievement has been shown to be an indispensable formational stimulus; without it, in fact, physical training cannot be accomplished. One has become mistrustful of achievement because of its limitation to certain measurable forms, and because of the careless striving for achievement which does not even stop short of physical damage, does not care at all about its effect on people as long as a new record can be set up. (We must explain that in order to make things plain everything is expressed very strongly here; there are many athletes for whom the record does not play such a role.)

To make use of achievement correctly the most important principle to be followed is that it must always be related to a definite person. In physical education we must always seek relative, not absolute, achievement. Eight-year-old children are not thought to be inferior because they cannot attain in running any extraordinary achievements expressed in seconds. The achievements of children must never be judged by their distance from the national, European, or world record but, at most, by the average for the age-level concerned.

It is very important to ensure that certain aspects of achievement are specially emphasized at certain stages of development.

For example, stamina and strength are achievements specifically for adults; speed on the other hand is for children and young people. The fastest speeds are simply unattainable beyond a certain age; the greatest stamina is physiologically impossible under a certain age. Children should be brought up to have a certain degree of stamina but it would be wrong to lay too much stress on stamina in childhood. All this is connected with the characteristic course of development; the bodily organs do not develop regularly, but by stages. This is why definite kinds of achievement are so clearly in the foreground at certain stages of development. They must be cultivated at precisely this time because they represent a necessary stimulus to growth which must be given if complete development is to be attained. At another time the same stimulus would have no effect.

These biologically determined rules for achievement in physical education are indispensable because they alone provide all the stimuli necessary for growth. So one should not strive for as little physical achievement as possible 'so that there is enough strength for intellectual achievement'; the capacity for intellectual achievement is not lessened but assured by good health. It is completely wrong to surmise that intellectual achievement can be heightened by simply suppressing physical achievement. If physical achievement is prevented intellectual achievement will also suffer.

To summarize the discussion so far: it is a question of applying the stimulus of achievement correctly as a means of physical education. It is safer not to strive for the best possible achievement, but only for the best possible achievement for the individual—always relating the achievement to a particular person. Further, it is safer to try to increase the capacity for achievement in all important fields to a high level but not the highest, so that one has varied, not one-sided, capacity for achievement; and finally, not to narrow achievement down to competitive sports but to try to teach the pupil to be just as skilful under changing external conditions, remaining flexible, not confined within the bounds of skills for specific situations. So, if achievement means the reaction set up in the pupil, physical education definitely needs achievement and cannot give it up because this would be giving up its effectiveness.

The question now arises as to whether achievement, in the

sense of work done, has any importance for physical education. The teacher must remember that achievement is not there for its own sake but as a means of stimulating growth. Yet—can he make the pupil increase his achievement to the necessary degree if he presents it to him only as a means of developing physically? Will a healthy pupil want to run more quickly or a longer distance because this means that his heart and lungs receive a growth stimulus? Or will he want to learn to do a difficult vault over the box because this teaches his nervous system to work better and makes him more skilful? Scarcely: the most important thing for the pupil is the feeling of enjoyment he gets from finding his powers growing in this or that activity. Strong, healthy young people are unwilling to accept exercises which are 'health giving'. So the real reason for the teacher's wishing to attain some achievement does not appeal to the pupil.

This too, of course, is expressed in an exaggerated manner. If the physical work is basically well constructed, pupils, especially the older ones, make no difficulty about doing some exercises because they are health giving, but this incentive can never be the only one for physical exercise.

It would be a bad thing if the teacher really made his pupils do the exercises only because they were health giving but had to pretend to them that he was interested in achievement for its own sake. This is not the case. Achievement must be encouraged for the physical effects on the body but the teacher never deals with the body alone, he looks at the whole person, and it is of value to him educationally to be able to exploit young people's enthusiasm for physical activities. A teacher is no educator unless he perceives what a 'point of attack' he has in doing physical activities with his pupils for furthering their whole education. So, when considering how physical education should be designed to further physical development the exercises are judged according to their physical effect; but when looking at the education of the whole person they are not done for this one reason, but for this reason along with many others.

Thus achievement conceived as work is also important for physical education. Now it becomes quite clear how fruitful the realization is that we always have to deal with the whole person. It is not necessary to *pretend* that every physical achievement is also an intellectual one—it really is. Winning a game is a physical achievement but in addition how much self-discipline, honesty, selfless co-operation among the players, is hidden in it! A hike which proceeds as it should, beginning with punctual arrival at the meeting place and continuing without arguments, with mutual aid and consideration, without unnecessary noise, happily, is a fine achievement which demands a great deal of work to make it possible. To cover a distance in as short a time as possible is mainly a physical achievement; it is not hiking in the real meaning of the word. A jump, which not only takes the pupil over a respectable height because he is a good jumper but which also has good form, is an achievement. A little dance, which turns out as neat as a nicely sung song, which is danced in the same way that a poem is recited, whose spirit one has understood—that is an achievement. Nothing else should be called achievement in physical education.

The reason then for describing something to the pupil as an achievement lies in its moral content; if this is lacking one does not speak of achievement. Many activities which one thinks of as moral or intellectual contain a large physical element. Think how much physical achievement there is in the playing of a violin or piano concerto by an artist, or when one person saves another's life, or in a difficult operation carried out by a surgeon, or in tending an invalid. Many other examples could be given to remind one that purely intellectual achievements are completed only by means of physical movement. However, it cannot be said that a person has achieved something just because there is a physical achievement in it. One can decide whether something is an achievement or not only on ethical grounds, otherwise one confuses the pupil's values—either the intellectual or the physical will seem inferior to him, both of which would be wrong. Whether work has been done or not from a physiological point of view tells one nothing about the value of the work.

Seen thus it is, for example, just as important for the general education of a pupil to work at forming his movements well as to learn to play an instrument, both of which depend on delicacy of movement. When the pupil, under the direction of the teacher, works to improve his posture, this is a piece of self-education; when he has attained good posture—which is not possible without self-discipline—he has really achieved something.

From this point of view suitable progressions are absolutely necessary. When playing an instrument, a pupil makes no progress if his teacher continually makes him play pieces which are too easy, and it is the same in physical education. It is possible that the physical exertion is great enough to release enough stimulus for growth, but the pupil has too little to do. A simple running game could provide enough work for the organs of respiration, even for older pupils, but it would not suffice: the task is too 'easy'. A game such as Prisoners' Base on the other hand, which has complicated rules and demands decisions in continually changing situations, and at the same time includes the exertion of running, would be a suitable task and the pupils' powers would grow through it. The work becomes aimless and unsatisfying if the pupils never feel they are making progress, and that the only reason for playing or jumping, running and throwing, is that it is health giving.

In the major games it is much easier to see whether the pupils are being presented with a real task and even a minor game is continually presenting new situations to be mastered. Suitable progressions are, however, especially important in skill practices or gymnastic tasks, where the teacher makes the pupils practise some vault or throw or sets climbing tasks or indicates a movement trick. If he does not discover how to increase the demands correctly he will not gain the lasting interest of the pupils.

Achievement, understood as meaning work, must not be neglected. The pupils must learn to achieve, and they can judge their powers only by a completed work. The only care of the educator is that the pupils should not over-value a purely physical ability, which they may have naturally, such as the power to jump high; they must also appreciate what they themselves have contributed to the achievement by their own effort and hard work.

It is probably scarcely necessary to say that all these reflections are equally valid for boys and girls. Girls too must achieve something in physical education, otherwise the work is merely play. In serious work on real achievement all vain self-representation vanishes because there is no energy or time for it, but to understand this as meaning high achievement in the form of measurements and scores would be completely wrong.

There could be moral dangers in achievement thus conceived. The pupils might learn to chase after records, or be led away from intellectual pursuits. If these educationally undesirable effects appear, achievement as such is probably not to blame, but has been incorrectly applied. Teachers of physical education must learn to use achievement correctly and the other teachers too must learn to see that one cannot completely exclude from physical education something which plays an essential role in the rest of education. They must be shown that it is possible to bring forth the necessary achievement without endangering educational principles; and that when this condition is fulfilled the physical education teacher accomplishes as much for the general education of young people, with his demands for achievement, as any other teacher.

Achievement, correctly understood, is thus indispensable in physical education; without it physical education becomes ineffective from a biological point of view, and merely trifling from an educational point of view.

Right from the beginning it must be emphasized that a principle which is already widely recognized in physical education for men is also valid for women: that is, that the whole variety of physical activities evolved by a nation should be considered as appropriate for their physical education. Only these physical activities which have evolved in a long historical process are broad and thorough enough to appeal to the nature of each new generation, and educate it thoroughly and from all sides.

This change of standpoint makes it possible to discuss the matter of physical education for women fruitfully. In his efforts to define the concept 'physical exercises' clearly, Gaulhofer (and Streicher, 1930) has shown that one must first ask oneself what in fact brings about physical formation in life. Physical exercises are not what people institute for the purpose of physical training, but everything which supplies biologically profitable stimuli. Physical education, like education in general, takes place everywhere in human life for it is a necessary expression of life in every human community. Planned, intentional education only forms a thin top layer of the great whole 'education', and for a long time it has been over-valued, indeed sometimes even taken for the whole of education. On the other hand the importance of this top layer must not be underestimated; by it one works into the totality of education what comes to us from the capacity for reflection. 'Man is the only creature who knows that he is,' says Jaspers (1932). The consciousness of an historical position and the task imposed by it is not insignificant for further development. To a certain extent we can direct this development. If this were not so there would be no conscious education. Free will is to be seen in the field of human education in the fact that the will is capable of taking effect.

Unconscious education does not follow principles. Perhaps there is in it an obedience to some laws which we must gradually learn to understand and exploit. However, conscious education follows principles and must do so—only this gives it consistency and point and the possibility of influencing the future. The more clearly and simply these principles are expressed, the more quickly and surely we will come to a unified, thorough physical education of the nation.

Conscious education becomes fixed in special structures, and institutions come into being whose main purpose, or at least a very important subsidiary purpose, is to cultivate physical exercise. If these institutions, e.g., schools, colleges and sports clubs, were to follow different principles this would be a sad waste of time and energy, for they are all concerned to educate the same people. If the principles are correct they are generally binding; otherwise they are either incorrect, or are rules for a special case, not principles.

The first principle for the physical education of women, which has already been hinted at above, is variety of exercise material. For a long time women worked with a traditional stock of exercises which were, it is true, gradually improved and broadened but which were never questioned from the point of view of principles. One did not consider which section of human movement they represented, or whether this section was the best possible. Yet such an examination of the material is necessary from time to time so as not to stagnate in tradition but always to work from the actual needs. The great variety of outdoor activities such as hiking, camping, swimming and the various kinds of water sports are among the most important branches of exercise; also games—individual and team—skiing and skating as far as circumstances permit. Folk dancing must not be omitted—from the children's singing games to the dances which are still enjoyed by adults. And the last but not the least important field one must mention—the activities peculiar to mankind, in the variety of their purposeful and artistic forms. All the activities which grow out of man's capacity to move forwards (walking, running, jumping, mounting, climbing, hanging) and his ability to handle objects (lifting, carrying, throwing, pulling, pushing) must form a part of the exercise material. Women's physical education must never become limited to gymnastics or to a stock of exercises based mainly on dancing.

The second most important principle is that of working in breadth. It is common experience that when one has finally got women to exercise they soon give up again out of a feeling of inadequacy. They measure their achievements against a sporting or gymnastic record and are discouraged to see the distance which separates them from it. They do not realize that they are applying the wrong standard. Sporting records are always for those who are highly talented physically; those with average capabilities will never reach them however hard they practise. Usually too they are attainable only during a short period of time at a youthful age.

If one were to try to base the work on such records it would be of little importance for most people. Success must be seen more in the increase of strength and skill, of joy in life and work, than in measurable achievements. If the work is good and varied, achievements that can be measured will also arise and will be welcomed by those exercising—but one must learn to evaluate them in comparison with the originally lower standard of performance, not with a 'record' which lies in infinity for ordinary people. In all aspects of the work a sensible furthering of the good average must always be the rule. Marks for achievement, competitions, etc., must be so framed that they assure good performance for many people, not top performances for the few. Here it is obvious to what extent a consciously set up principle influences the work. The principle of working in breadth fits in with the irrational striving to measure one's powers, which will always be present in healthy young girls. This striving is not repressed or silenced but is taken up and guided. Competitions based on breadth of work look different from those framed out of the desire for top achievements.

Another generally binding principle is that all physical education for women must also be education for a healthy way of life. This means first that the teaching itself must be framed in a way that is in complete harmony with principles of good health. The exercise places must be light and airy, kept scrupulously clean, and provided with washing facilities which are regularly used. Meal times in relation to the periods of exercise and the length of the exercise periods should not be considered of secondary importance. All these facets of physical education help to create good habits and this is part of good education. The clothing worn during exercise should be suitable and practical, and can be the starting-point for thoughts on healthy clothing in daily life and work. The idea of educating the pupils in health also includes the rejection of alcohol and tobacco, which have now been proved to be harmful to procreation even when they are taken in moderation. As in general, so in physical education for women absolutely every danger to health must be avoided. Life usually brings some unavoidable damage with it (lack of light and air in the city, too much and too heavy work, illness) but physical exercise must be so arranged that it improves health. Women owe this to future generations.

However, in all this health education sullen, peevish preaching must be avoided. The healthy life is the obvious one, about which there is as little need to speak as about truthfulness or cleanliness. One must show the blessings which radiate from it, the freedom and easiness of life in contrast to the evils of excess or being hidebound by unintelligent tradition.

In physical education it is absolutely vital that girls should be taught to understand the physical side of bringing up children. The way a child learns to stand and walk, the importance of sufficient room to play, plenty of time for playing and sensibly chosen mobile toys—all this must be made clear. It is vital that mothers should know what has long been known by science about posture and breathing and that they should not hammer incorrect ideas into their children's heads in all good faith, just because they have never learnt what is right.

Besides these principles we must discuss another one, which is very important but not easy to explain: it is that of setting one's face against spectator orientation. Jahn has said that: 'The gymnastic area is not a stage and nobody has the right to expect a play on it'. Much that is unpleasing has entered women's gymnastics because very often too little thought was given to those exercising and too much to the spectators. For the purpose of display, beautiful or emotionally exciting groups were brought together; practising with these groups took a lot of time and effort, especially when large numbers were involved, and the ordinary exercises came more and more under the laws of display without its always being noticed.

Any organization, which just seeks to impress the public on festive occasions with displays, is not being criticized, for we do not mean that displays should not be given. Of course performances must be well prepared and exercises must be done which make a good show. Those who take part, because they are 'representatives', must appear in good order with faultless bearing. However, the festive nature of the event rests less on a certain choice of exercises than on the fact that they are built into the frame of the festival, which is governed by a unified idea. Combining and drilling in symmetrical groups or changing movements to follow supposed laws of beauty, is a false path; splendour of formation does not depend on this. A beautiful bunch of flowers, which is to adorn a festival, does not result from the flowers being dyed or bound together in strict symmetry.

It is necessary in each case to decide whether one is preparing a display or doing exercises with people for their own benefit. Basically there is a lack of clarity here, something has not been thought out properly. It was felt that there must be room in women's physical education for the creative powers, and that enough had been done to fulfil this need by giving displays. One looked for the beauty outside instead of within.

Creative work has deep importance in the life of the individual and the people, it is not idle trifling. To take all art from the culture of the nation would mean monstrous impoverishment. The field of physical education reaches into the field of art because movement, like stone, colour, sound, etc., can become a material for creative work. Thorough education of the body must not just train movement in an objective way as a means to practical purposes, but must also leave space for shaping the material—in this case movement. Movement is a material as ancient and common to all mankind as the voice, which is used for communication but which also gives expression to intellectual matters when elevated in song and poetry. This means that dancing and 'dancing play with movement' are an essential, indispensable constituent of all thorough physical education, right from the beginning up to the final stage of education.

Where movement is purposeful, in locomotion for example, it is, like all work, subject to the law of the conservation of energy and its purposefulness is its beauty. When one begins to shape it, the material must be seen in its special beauty and individual possibilities. This is not easy with movement because it is an always changing, evanescent material, not a stable one. Yet just as the professional artist has to learn to work within the bounds of his material—the only protection against trash—so one does here. One must gradually learn to *see* human movement, only then can one shape it in accordance with its inner laws. This is a different matter from preparing displays which in turn have their own aesthetic laws, and the two must not be confused.

What should education do in this field? Art always expresses something of man's innermost being. So in dancing too the image of woman, which we rate above education, is to be seen. There are a number of things which one would not take exception to from the point of view of health, but which must nevertheless be rejected because they present an image of woman which has nothing to do with the growth and prospering of the nation. The attitude of pleasing at any price, descending to the level of sensation-seeking spectators—these are things which must be rejected as being symbolical of a certain state of mind: a state of mind which is expressed by Nietzsche crudely but effectively in his contrast of two types of women, mother and whore.

Here it becomes clear that the scientific basis given by anatomy and physiology is not enough for devising a system of physical education for women. It is true that it provides facts which one cannot forget with impunity. Practical work is strictly tied to this scientific basis and should be thought out even better physiologically. One cannot tend any living creature without knowing its natural needs, but this is not enough. Whilst the work is built up from the physical side alone it is not 'complete'. Affectation in movement does no harm to heart and lungs but it may harm the person. In a profound sense this kind of movement is not 'healthy'.

In this branch of physical education, best described as dancing play with movement, orientation to the spectator destroys all educational value. A pretty picture is not the aim—the pupils must try to create in the familiar material of movement just as they try in sounds or colours, and thus they will experience the joy of artistic activity, which is so much deeper than passive enjoyment and which can so enrich life. This joy is not to be had as cheaply as the applause of easily satisfied spectators. 'One cannot demand truthfulness of women as long as one teaches them to believe that their principal aim in life is—to please' (Ebner-Eschenbach).

Anyone who has the opportunity to compare the physical education of today and yesterday will immediately notice great differences in the lessons, differences which seem to go far beyond
the individual characteristics imparted by the teacher. Far-reaching changes are under way which cannot be said to be complete
but which have proceeded far enough for one to be able to see
their line of development. Pupils learn to play individual and
team games, to dance, to swim, take part in various kinds of
sports, hike and camp. They may even have the opportunity to
learn canoeing, skating, skiing or other outdoor activities. In
gymnastics too things are proceeding quite differently. Exercises
which make varied demands on the body predominate: mounting
and climbing, pulling and pushing, throwing, running and jumping agility and vaulting exercises on apparatus, which used to
be cultivated almost exclusively, have not disappeared, but now
they constitute only a part of the exercise material. Contrived,
jerky exercises have been replaced by purposeful, flowing movements which include every part of the body. Standing about waiting has disappeared and the lessons are alive and rich in movement.

It might be thought that this enlarging of the material is no
more important in physical education than in any other subject,
but this is not so; here it means a deepening of the work and
greatly increased effectiveness. The former narrow physical
training had very limited physical goals; it was aimed at strength
and a particular kind of skill. Yet it would not be easy to give a
reason for the emphasis laid on these particular physical achievements; they are not of special importance either for health or
in practical work. The term 'muscular power' which was characteristic of the old gymnastics was replaced by the term 'organic
power' which rightly emphasizes the importance of good development of heart and lungs. Of course this new aim represented
progress but it needed a lot more before one could speak of
really thorough physical training. One was learning to understand that people are a unity, and recognizing that only a training which comprehends all the powers really improves health.

From this point of view the lively forms of physical exercise which make a wide variety of demands on the body, like hiking, games, swimming, etc., are far superior to gymnastics which emphasize individual movements. As long as these are absent from the work it cannot claim to be general physical education.

The much greater effectiveness of modern physical education compared with the work in the past is based on its variety. The old gymnastics had cut a small part out of the great field of 'physical exercise'—not even a general part, open to everyone, as for example hiking would have been, but a specialist part, vaulting and agility work on apparatus, which requires certain physical and mental talents. Without these a person is not permanently attracted; he may understand the simple gymnastic tricks but he will never reach a high level because he has no inner stimulus for practice. Without practice his development is cut off in this field, and after a certain time he ceases to make progress. Progress is indispensable if one is to remain faithful to physical exercise; no one repeats the exercise he can already do over and over again—just because it is good for him. The urge to play is stronger and a more effective stimulus than reason; the number of real 'health gymnasts' is probably not very high. If one does not make enough progress in a field to enable one to play, one's impulse to play is not satisfied and as a result it moves to another field. Only through play (as described by Schiller, 1794) does a field become inexhaustible and therefore attractive; a desire for free participation only comes with a certain degree of ability. It is the same with physical exercise; this is why gymnastic tricks on apparatus have a lasting appeal only for people with whose physical and psychological make-up they correspond; only such people attain a degree of facility which allows them to play whilst exercising. The others experience in a painful way the limits of their ability—and this is not what people are looking for in their leisure activities, for gymnastics must also be considered in this category. Gymnastics, requiring a certain natural aptitude, grip and attract lastingly only people of a certain type. Thus, from the point of view of numbers alone, gymnastics are effective for fewer people than physical education which is wide and includes many fields, and can therefore give something to people with different aptitudes. The special stamp of each individual is often struck when he is still a child, certainly at puberty; this means that the work in school must have breadth and variety; it must provide a general training and, over and above that, must open the way for each person to find some favourite physical activity which he can take with him into life. This is one of the most important tasks of physical education; if it can be achieved something of inestimable value will have been contributed to culture.

Over the past years an upsurge of interest in physical activities has arisen independently of the schools. One has only to look at the demand for sporting facilities or at the numbers of people going to the countryside at the weekends, to appreciate this interest. Just compare the space formerly allotted to the sporting news in the press with the space this occupies today. These changes do not mean that the school must not 'waste its time' on physical exercise any longer; it means that the school has a cultural task to fulfil: that of giving the work an intellectual content. Physical exercise does not have to be unintellectual; this is no part of its nature but only of the way in which many people carry it out. As part of their educational work, the schools should undertake to lead their pupils in culturally acceptable forms of physical exercise which are biologically necessary for the individual and, with the ever increasing process of mechanization, indispensable for the health of the nation. The schools must not evade this task.

Hitherto the schools have not always felt responsible for the form in which their pupils carry out physical exercise but in future they will have to do so. The unedifying aspects of much physical activity today are not entirely the fault of the schools except that they have tended to evade this responsibility despite the fact that the term 'harmonious education' is continually on everyone's lips. The schools will have to be made responsible and give their pupils a lead in this field which contains so many dangers (not only physical) and which has an irresistible appeal for young people, with all their vitality. Physical exercise is necessary for the body and its intellectual effect depends upon how it is done; this is a question of how it is organized.

Now physical activities such as games, hiking, skiing, swimming, etc., which used to form only a small part of the physical education programme in schools, are precisely the types most necessary for health and most attractive to young people; they are also the ones which have had the greatest upsurge in recent years. The schools must not let their pupils leave without having given them understanding and aroused their sense of how physical exercise should be done. Lacking this leadership young people may fall prey to all kinds of degenerate forms of physical activity without even noticing that they are on the wrong path. The ideas outlined here show that this constitutes an essential cultural task for the schools.

The broadening of the material of physical education makes it possible for the schools, indeed makes it their duty, to be carriers of culture, even into the field of biologically necessary physical exercise. This is a difficult but splendid task.

Appendix

The following is a complete reference list to those passages, originally contributed by Dr Streicher to Austrian publications, which make up this volume.

Section I:
Natürliches Turnen, Vol. III, pp. 116–19
—Vol. V, pp. 16–17
—Vol. III, pp. 119–27
—Vol. I, pp. 146–53
—Vol. V, pp. 67–69
—Vol. I, pp. 108–9
—Vol. III, p. 118
—Vol. I, pp. 109–10
—Vol. V, pp. 69–72
—Vol. V, pp. 8–13
—Vol. I, pp. 161–88

Section II:
Grundzüge des österreichischen Schulturnens, Section III, pp. 102–3
Natürliches Turnen, Vol. III, pp. 18–19
Grundzüge des österreichischen Schulturnens, Section III, pp. 103–17
Natürliches Turnen, Vol. III, pp. 19–25
Grundzüge des österreichischen Schulturnens, Section III, pp. 123–6
Natürliches Turnen, Vol. III, pp. 8–12
—Vol. III, pp. 86–88
—Vol. V, pp. 104–6
—Vol. III, p. 89
—Vol. V, pp. 52–54
—Vol. V, pp. 63–67
—Vol. V, p. 55
—Vol. V, pp. 31–35

Section III:
Natürliches Turnen, Vol. III, pp. 108–11
—Vol. II, pp. 169–75

Section III :
—Vol. II, pp. 34–50
—Vol. I, pp. 199–202
—Vol. I, pp. 204–5
—Vol. V, pp. 143–53
—Vol. III, pp. 66–77
—Vol. III, pp. 129–35
—Vol. II, pp. 106–10

Glossary

Art forms. A complex series of movements which have developed from the purposeful functional activities as through the ages man has enjoyed himself with movement in his ceremonies, folk festivals, leisure hours, etc. Two kinds of art forms can be distinguished:

(*a*) the acrobatic forms, e.g., vaulting, tumbling, fancy diving, juggling.

(*b*) the beautiful forms expressing a spiritual content in movement, i.e., all forms of dancing including the preparatory forms of dancing.

Formative exercises. Exercises by means of which the best personal form of movement and posture is to be attained.

Functional activities. Purposeful movements used in daily life and work, generally comprehensible by their names: i.e., movements concerned with locomotion such as walking, running, mounting and climbing, etc., and movements concerned with handling objects such as pulling, pushing, lifting, throwing, etc.

Gymnastik. Began in the first third of the twentieth century in Germany. Drama (Delsarte), dance (Duncan, Laban), music (Dalcroze, Bode) and singing (Rotenburger Schule) are at its roots; efforts to reform the mode of life were added, often combined with the philosophy of L. Klages. By its individually orientated work *Gymnastik* was in contrast to *Turnen*, which aimed at appealing to the masses, and to *Sport* with its tendency to set up records. Each of the *Gymnastik* systems developed its own working method; nevertheless it could be said that indoor work, no apparatus, use of music and emphasis on good movement were characteristic features. The pioneers tried to keep up a high level of work, but as private institutions the schools were dependent on their 'customers' and were forced, again and again, to compromise.

Partial movement. Part of a functional activity practised in order to improve the whole.

Bibliography

Braus, H., *Anatomie des Menschen*, Vol. 1, Bewegungsapparat, J. Springer, Berlin, 1921

Braus, H. and Elze, C., *Anatomie des Menschen*, Vol. 3, Zentrales Nervensystem, J. Springer, Berlin, 1932

Brelthaupt, R. M., *Die natürliche Klaviertechnik*, Kahnt, Leipzig, 1921

Brücke, E. T., *Vom biologischen Sinn des Sportes*, J. Springer, Vienna, 1926

Buytendijk, F. J. J., *Allgemeine Theorie der menschlichen Haltung und Bewegung*, J. Springer, Berlin, 1956

Durig, A., *Über die physiologischen Grundlagen der Atemübungen*, J. Springer, Vienna, 1931

Fischer, O., see Braus, H., *Anatomie des Menschen*, Vol. 1, Bewegungsapparat, J. Springer, Berlin, 1921

Friedel, A., 'Der Einfluss der Nasenatmung auf die Form des Brustkorbés', *Die Leibesübungen*, No. 5, p. 117, Weidmann, Berlin, 1930

Gaulhofer, K. and Streicher, M., *Grundzüge des österreichischen Schulturnens*, Verlag für Jugend und Volk, Vienna, 1922, latest ed. 1950

Kinderturnstunden für das 1. Schuljahr, Verlag für Jugend und Volk, Vienna, 1927, 1950

Natürliches Turnen, Volume II, Verlag für Jugend und Volk, Vienna, 1930, 1949

Natürliches Turnen, Volume I, Verlag für Jugend und Volk, Vienna, 1931, 1949

Kinderturnstunden für das 3. Schuljahr, Verlag für Jugend und Volk, Vienna, 1932, 1950

Kinderturnstunden für das 4. Schuljahr, Verlag für Jugend und Volk, Vienna, 1935, 1950

Haglund, P., *Prinzipien der Orthopädie*, Gustav Fischer, Jena, 1923

Hartmann, N., *Kleinere Schriften I*, Walter de Gruyter, Berlin, 1924

Heuss, T., *Was ist Qualität?* Rainer Wunderlich, Hermann Leins, Tübingen, 1951

Hofbauer, L., *Atmungspathologie und-therapie*, J. Springer, Berlin, 1921

Hörnicke, E., 'Atmung und Leistungsfähigkeit', *Münchner Medizinische Wochenschrift*, Vol. 71, No. 45, p. 1569, November 1924

'Der Übungsfaktor in der menschlichen Atmung', *Münchner Medizinische Wochenschrift*, Vol. 72, No. 32, p. 1332, August 1925

'Der Einfluss des Atmungstypus auf den Organismus der Frau', *Münchner Medizinische Wochenschrift*, Vol. 73, No. 5, p. 190, January 1926

Jaspers, K., *Die geistige Situation der Zeit*, Walter de Gruyter, Berlin–Leipzig, 1932

Klages, L., *Ausdrucksbewegung und Gestaltungskraft*, W. Engelmann, Leipzig, 1921

Klatt, F., *Die geistige Wendung des Maschinenzeitalters*, Alfred Protte, Potsdam, 1930

Kleist, H., *'Über das Marionettentheater'*, Quelle-Bücherei, Verlag für Jugend und Volk, Vienna, 1810, 1924

Krueger, F. and Klemm, O., 'Motorik', *Neue psychologische Studien*, C. H. Beck'sche Verlagsbuchhandlung, München, 1933

Lange, F., 'Die Haltungsschäden und die Leibesübungen', *Das Münchner Sonderturnen*, J. F. Lehmann, München, 1928

Lange, W. G., *Überfunktionelle Anpassung*, J. Springer, Berlin, 1917

Magnus, R., *Körperstellung*, J. Springer, Berlin, 1924

Nohl, H., *Die ästhetische Wirklichkeit*, Schulte-Bulmke, Frankfurt--am-Main, 1935

Okunewa, J. J., Steinbach, E. E. and Schtscheglowa, L. N., 'Physiologische Untersuchung zur Frage der hygienischen Normierung des Hebens und Tragens von Lasten durch Frauen', *Arbeits-Physiologie*, Vol. 2, No. 6, p. 434, J. Springer, Berlin, 1930

Pallat, L., 'Die Kunsterziehung', *Nohl-Pallat, Handbuch der Pädagogik*, Vol. III, p. 425, J. Beltz, Langensalza, 1930

Pallat, L. and Hilker, F., *Künstlerische Körperschulung*, F. Hirt, Breslau, 1923, 1926

Pestalozzi, H., *Einleitung auf den Versuch einer Elementargymnastik*, J. Beltz, Langensalza, 1807, 1924, 1962

Plessner, H., 'Die Deutung des mimischen Ausdrucks', *Zwischen Philosophie und Gesellschaft*, Francke, Bern, 1953

'Die Funktion des Sportes in der industriellen Gesellschaft', *Wissenschaft und Weltbild*, December 1956, p. 262, Österreichischer Bundesverlag, Vienna

Plügge, H., *Grazie und Anmut*, Claassen und Goverts, Hamburg, 1947

Schiller, F., 'Über die ästhetische Erziehung des Menschengeschlechtes', *Schillers Werke*, Vol. 8, p. 224, Bibliographisches Institut, Leipzig–Vienna, 1794

Spitzy, H., *Die körperliche Erziehung des Kindes*, Urban und Schwarzenberg, Vienna–Berlin, 1914, 1928
'Gefahren bei Überbeanspruchung der Wirbelsäule', *Natürliches Turnen*, Vol. IV, p. 225, Verlag für Jugend und Volk, Vienna, 1956

Spranger, E., *Psychologie des Jugendalters*, Quelle und Meyer, Leipzig, 1924
'Lehrer und Lehrerpersönlichkeit', *Natürliches Turnen*, Vol. IV, Verlag für Jugend und Volk, Vienna, 1956

Steinemann, J., 'Natürlicher und unnatürlicher Bewegungsstil', *Schweizer Zeitschrift, Die Körpererziehung*, Vol. 2, P. Haupt, Bern, 1924

Straus, E., *Vom Sinn der Sinne*, J. Springer, Berlin, 1956

Streicher, M., *Kinderturnstunden für das 2. Schuljahr*, Verlag für Jugend und Volk, Vienna, 1927, 1951
Natürliches Turnen, Volume III, Verlag für Jugend und Volk, Vienna, 1942, 1950
Natürliches Turnen, Volume IV, Verlag für Jugend und Volk, Vienna, 1956
Natürliches Turnen, Volume V, Verlag für Jugend und Volk, Vienna, 1959, 1961
'Systematik und Bewegungslehre', *Festschrift für C. Diem*, Wilhelm Limpert, Frankfurt-Vienna, 1962
'Ästhetik der Bewegung', *Neue Sammlung*, Vol. 5, 1966. Also contained in *Report of the Fifth International Congress, International Association of Physical Education and Sports for Girls and Women*, 'The Adolescents of Today', pp. 28–35, Karl Hofmann, Stuttgart, 1966

Thulin, J. G., *Kleinkinderturnen mit Übungsschatz und Stundenbildern für das 6. bis 8. Lebensjahr*, Translated by F. Lösel, P. Eberhardt, Leipzig, 1925

Tumlirz, *Einführung in die Jugendkunde*, Vol. 1, Julius Klink-
hardt, Leipzig, 1920
Wachholder, K., *Willkürliche Haltung und Bewegung*, Bergmann,
München, 1928
Weizsäcker, V., *Der Gestaltkreis*, Thieme, Leipzig, 1940
Winther, F., *Körperbildung als Kunst und Pflicht*, Delphin,
München, 1914, 1923
Wundt, W., *System der Philosophie I*, W. Engelmann, Leipzig,
1907
Zeitschrift 'Gymnastik', 1926–33, Brandenburgische Verlags-
anstalt, Berlin–Schöneberg

Index